GW00669810

The Little Book
of
EROTICA

The Little Book
of

EROTICA

Edited by
Alison Bullivant

SIENA

This edition published and distributed by Siena, 1999

Siena is an imprint of Parragon

Parragon
Queen Street House
4 Queen Street
Bath BA1 1HE

Produced by Magpie Books, an imprint of
Robinson Publishing Ltd, London

ISBN 0 75252 768 1

A copy of the British Library Cataloguing-in-
Publication Data is available from the British Library
Printed in China

Contents

Introduction

Art has treated erotic themes at almost all periods, because eroticism lies at the root of all human life.

Edward Fuchs

The word erotica derives from the Greek, eros, meaning sexual love. Our desire for sex (and therefore procreation) is the greatest motivator of the human race, greater even than survival. It is understandable therefore that the celebration of it should dominate art, or even be its lifeblood.

Erotic art is simply a reflection of the sexual culture of the time. The majority of sexual expression that was at one time taboo is now sold and read openly. Imagery we see in paintings, photographs and films, and that

which is evoked from the printed page, might once have been considered pornographic, rather than simply pleasurable or informative. As a New York Times *headline stated recently:* Yesterday's smut is today's erotica.

Individual tastes vary and some erotic practices stimulate whilst others leave one cold. Flagellation, for example, however anaphrodisiac it may seem to some, was once regarded as a normal and acceptable sexual stimulant, and it is too important a subject (especially in English erotic literature) to exclude from this book. However, there is no serious sadomasochism in here, and no animals or children, so if that is your disposition you will have to look elsewhere.

The Little Book of Erotica *is a tribute to sexual love, with a diverse collection of extracts from fiction, autobiography and poetry culled from nearly 2000 years of history, from the Romans and the ancient Eastern civilizations up to the Victorian era.*

When all is done I find that love is

nothing else but an insatiate thirst of enjoying greedily a desired subject. Nor Venus that good huswife, other than a tickling delight of emptying one's seminary vessels: as is the pleasure which nature giveth us to discharge other parts, which becommeth faulty by immoderation and defective by indiscretion.

Michel Montaigne (1522–92), Essais

THE COMIC-EROTIC

When sex and comedy are combined the result is generally anaphrodisiac or anti-erotic, but the Greeks and the Romans, particularly the Romans, were very good at producing amusing erotic literature, especially in verse form. Bawdiness was popular again in the Middle Ages, the early sixteenth century and the Renaissance, but the Victorians were very stuffy about it, and there is little to amuse there. Some pieces excerpted here, such as Frances Grose's Classical Dictionary of the Vulgar Tongue, *were no doubt written in all seriousness, but now make for amusing reading.*

Just now I found a young boy
stuffing his girl,

I rose, naturally, and
(with a nod to Venus)
fell and transfixed him there
with a good stiff prick,
like his own.

Catullus (c. 84–c. 54 BC)

from *Amores, Book III*

~

She'd looks, she'd style,
I'd been after her for weeks.
There we were, lying there,
Cosying up – and nothing.
I wanted it, she wanted it –
And *could* I get it up?
She held me in her arms –
White snow they were, ivory –
We tongue-kissed, snuggled,
She called me "Rambo",
"Hammerdrill", you name it –
Nothing. I sagged: an icicle
(Except that icicles are stiff);
A deadweight, a dodo,
A pricked balloon.
At my age! Embarrassing.
And think of the future –
If I *have* a future. No joy.
Might as well take nuns to bed,
Baby sisters – no risk, no problem.

And this from me – *me*!
When I think of those kisses –
Oaks would have danced for them,
Stones would have swooned for them,
Steel would have, flesh would've –
Forget it. I must have been dead.
Lifeless, departed, defunct.
She was painting for the blind,
Singing for the deaf. I just lay there.
I did what I could. I *imagined*:
"Do *this*, put that *there*,
Now perhaps if we . . ." Nothing.
Limp. Yesterday's rose.
Whereas *now*! Thrusting, eager,
Bright-eyed and bushy-tailed and – late!
Stop *doing* that! Bastard!
Where were you when I needed you?
The things I do for you! The cash I spend!
She does her damnedest, takes you in hand,
Softly, softly, a million tricks –
And all you do is sulk. Gods, was she cross!

Publius Ovidius Naso (Ovid) (43 BC–AD 17)
Translated by Kenneth McLeish

The roomy Lydia's private parts surpass
The lusty dray horse' elephantine arse;
Wide as the schoolboy's ringing iron hoop;
Vast as the ring the agile riders stoop
And leap through neatly, touching not the
 side,
As round and round the dusty course they
 ride;
Capacious as some old and well-worn
 shoe,
That's trudged the muddy streets since first
 'twas new;
Stretched like the net the crafty fowler
 holds;
And drapery as a curtain's heavy folds;
Loose as the bracelet gemmed with green
 and scarlet,
That mocks the arm of some consumptive
 harlot;
Slack as a feather bed without the feathers;
And baggy as some ostler's well-used
 leathers;
Relaxed and hanging like the skinny coat

That shields the vulture's foul and flabby
   throat.
'Tis said, while bathing once we trod love's
   path,
I know not, but I seemed to fuck the bath.
Martial (c. AD 40– 104)

Castaway

∼

He grabbed me round my slender neck
I could not shout or scream
He carried me into his room
Where we could not be seen;
He tore away my flimsy wrap
And gazed upon my form –
I was so cold and still and damp,
While he was wet and warm.
His feverish mouth he pressed to mine –
I let him have his way –
He drained me of my very self,
I could not say him nay.

He made me what I am. Alas!
That's why you find me here . . .
A broken vessel – broken glass –
That once held Bottled Beer

Anon

Of an Heroical Answer of a
Great Roman Lady to Her Husband
~

A grave wise man that had a great rich lady,
Such as perhaps in these days found there
    may be,
Did think she played him false and more
    than think,
Save that in wisdom he thereat did wink.
Howbeit one time disposed to sport and play
Thus to his wife he pleasantly did say,
"Since strangers lodge their arrows in thy
    quiver,
Dear dame, I pray you yet the cause deliver,
If you can tell the cause and not dissemble,

How all our children me so much resemble?"
The lady blushed but yet this answer made
"Though I have used some traffic in the
    trade,
And must confess, as you have touched
    before
My bark was sometimes steered with foreign
    oar,
Yet stowed I no man's stuff but first
    persuaded
The bottom with your ballast full was laded."

John Harington (1561–1612)

Dildoes

~

Dildoes, without the least disgrace,
May well supply the lover's place,
And make our girls ne'er care for 't,
Though 'twere their fortune to go bare-foot.

Samuel Butler (1613–80)

from *Marriage-a-la Mode*

Whilst Alexis lay pressed
In her Arms he loved best
With his hands round her neck
And his head on her breast,
He found the fierce pleasure too hasty to
    stay,
And his soul in the tempest just flying away.

When Celia saw this,
With a sigh, and a kiss,
She cry'd, "Oh my dear, I am robbed of my
    bliss;
'Tis unkind to your Love, and unfaithfully
    done,
To leave me behind you, and die all alone."

The Youth, though in haste,
And breathing his last,
In pity died slowly, while she died more fast;
Till at length she cried, "Now, my dear, now
    let us go,

Now die, my Alexis, and I will die too."

Thus entranced they did lie,
Till Alexis did try
To recover new breath, that again he might
    die:
Then often they died; but the more they did
    so,
The Nymph died more quick, and the
    Shepherd more slow.

John Dryden (1631–1700)

from *The Emperor of the Moon*

~

All soft and sweet the maid appears,
With looks that know no art,
And though she yields with trembling fears,
She yields with all her heart.

Aphra Behn (1640–80)

from *A Satire on Charles II*

~

Peace is his aim, his gentleness is such,
And he loves love, for he loves screwing
   much.
Nor are his high desires above his strength:
His sceptre and his tool are of a length,
And she may sway the one who plays with
   t'other.
   John Wilmot, Earl of Rochester (1648–80)

Once, Twice, Thrice

~

Once, twice thrice, I Julia tried,
The scornful puss as oft denied,
And since I can no better thrive,
I'll cringe to ne'er a bitch alive.
So kiss my arse, disdainful sow!
Good claret is my mistress now.
                    17th-century English Catch Song

Now in his vigorous grasp, half-won she pants,
   Struggles, denies – yet in denying, grants!

Anon

LIMERICKS

King Louis gave a lesson in Class,
One time he was sexing a lass.
When she used the word "Damn"
He rebuked her: "Please ma'am,
Keep a more civil tongue in my ass."

1950

There was an old bugger of Como
Who suddenly cried: "Ecce homo!"
He tracked his man down
To the heart of the town,
And gobbled him off in the duomo.

1928

It's only human nature after all
If a fellow puts a girl against the wall
And puts his inclination
Into her accommodation
To increase the population
Of the rising generation –
Why, it's only human nature after all.

1943

An old couple just at Shrovetide
Were having a piece – when he died.
The wife for a week
Sat tight on his peak,
And bounced up and down as she cried.

1942

A maestro directing in Rome
Had a quaint way of driving it home.
Whoever he climbed
Had to keep her tail timed
To the beat of his old metronome.

1943

A pansy who lived in Khartoum
Took a lesbian up to his room,
And they argued all night
Over who had the right
To do what, and with which, and to whom.

1941

Il y avait un plombier, François,
Qui plombait sa femme dans le Bois.
Dit-elle, "Arretez!
J'entends quelqu'un venait."
Dit le plombier, en plombant, "C'est moi."

1941

from Frances Grose's *Classical Dictionary of the Vulgar Tongue*

~

Colloquial language, or slang, usually has a fairly short life-span, so it is astonishing to find how many "vulgar" terms from this dictionary, written in 1785, are still in use today. For example, a girl was a "piece," a girl who enjoyed sex was a "goer." "Tools" and "tackle" were a man's private parts; to have sex was to "screw" or "shag;" a "muff" referred to a woman's genitals. Interestingly though, some meanings like "punk" have changed completely; a "rascal" was a rogue or a villain but specifically a man without genitals. Here are some more examples from The Dictionary of the Vulgar Tongue.

Armour (to use "Mrs Philip's ware"): to wear a condom

Backgammon Player: a sodomite

Beard Splitter: a man much given to wenching

Biter: a wench whose cunt is ready to bite her arse: a lascivious, rampant wench

Buttocking Shop: a brothel

Cock Alley or Cock Lane: the private parts of a woman

Dry Bob: copulation without emission

Lobcock: a large relaxed penis

Piss-Proud: a false erection

Punk: a whore

To Roger: to bull, or lie with a woman; from the name of Roger being frequently given to a bull

Socket Money: a whore's fee

Wap: to copulate

Whirlygigs: testicles

Whorepipe: penis

EIGHT REASONS FOR CHOOSING
AN OLDER MISTRESS

~

From a letter written by Benjamin
Franklin to a friend in 1745

~

1. Because they have more knowledge of the world and their minds are better stored with observations, their conversation is more improving and more lastingly agreeable.

2. Because when women cease to be handsome they study to be good. To maintain their influence over men, they supply the diminution of beauty by an augmentation of utility. They learn to do a thousand services small and great, and are the most tender and useful of friends when you are sick. Thus they continue amiable. And hence there is hardly such a thing to be found as an old woman who is not a good woman.

3. Because there is no hazard of children, which irregularly produced may be attended with much inconvenience.

4. Because through more experience they are more prudent and discreet in conducting an intrigue to prevent suspicion. The commerce with them is therefore safer with regard to your reputation. And with regard to theirs, if the affair should happen to be known, considerate people might be rather inclined to excuse an old woman, who would kindly take care of a young man, form his manners by her good counsels, and prevent his ruining his health and fortune among mercenary prostitutes.

5. Because in every animal that walks upright the deficiency of the fluids that fill the muscles appears first in the highest part. The face first grows lank and wrinkled; then the neck; then the breast and arms; the lower parts continuing to the last as plump as ever: so

that covering all above with a basket, and regarding only what is below the girdle, it is impossible of two women to tell an old one from a young one. And as in the dark all cats are gray, the pleasure of corporal enjoyment with an old woman is at least equal, and frequently superior; every knack being, by practice, capable of improvement.

6. Because the sin is less. The debauching a virgin may be her ruin, and make her for life unhappy.

7. Because the compunction is less. The having made a young girl miserable may give you frequent bitter reflection; none of which can attend the making an old woman happy.

8th and lastly: They are so grateful!

FORBIDDEN LITERATURE OF THE VICTORIANS

Erotic writing has been banned at various times throughout history. This selection (except for Fanny Hill, *which was written in the previous century*) dates from the puritanical Victorian era when writers of sexual literature went underground. This explains why many erotic works produced during this time were anonymous or pseudonymous. A surprising number of these authors were said to have been "forced" by poverty into writing erotica, but whatever the motivation the material that has been unearthed proves that suppression serves to produce ever more explicit prose.

MEMOIRS OF A WOMAN OF
PLEASURE or FANNY HILL

~

John Cleland (1709–89) was another author of erotica who wrote for money, this time to pay off debts for which he had been imprisoned. Published in 1748–9, *Memoirs of a Woman of Pleasure*, more commonly known as *Fanny Hill*, has been called one of the finest examples of erotic realism in the English language. However, although the novel netted his publisher £10,000, Cleland received only 20 guineas. In writing *Fanny Hill*, Cleland set out to prove that he could write such a novel without using any obscene language. This he undoubtedly achieved, although it didn't prevent him from being summoned before the Privy Council for indecency.

Written from the comfortable vantage point of wealth and respectability, the female narrator (Fanny Hill) tells the story of her life. As a poor and innocent young girl, she is taken in by a brothel-keeper and is soon acquainted with the profession. Fanny becomes a kept woman and works as a "high class" prostitute, earning enough money to retire at the age of eighteen and to marry her love.

from *Fanny Hill*

~

Fanny has become the kept woman of Mr H., but she takes a fancy to a young country lad who has been taken into service by her master.

I first gave the youth a re-encouraging kiss, which he repaid me with a fervour that seemed at once to thank me and bribe my farther compliance, and I soon replaced myself in a posture to receive, at all risks, the renewed invasion, which he did not delay an instant; for, being presently remounted, I once more felt the smooth hard gristle forcing an entrance, which he achieved rather easier than before. Pained, however, as I was, with his efforts of gaining a complete admission, which he was so regardful as to manage by gentle degrees, I took care not to complain. In the meantime, the soft strait passage gradually loosens, yields, and, stretched to its utmost bearing by the stiff, thick, in-driven engine, sensible at once to the ravishing pleasure of the feel and the pain of the distension, let him in about half way, when all the most nervous activity he now exerted to further his penetration gained him not an inch of his purpose; for, whilst he hesitated there, the crisis of pleasure overtook him, and the close compressure of the warm surrounding fold drew from him the ecstatic gush, even before mine was ready to meet it, kept up by the pain I had endured in the course of the engagement, from the unsufferable size of his weapon, though it was not as yet in above half its length.

I expected then, but without wishing it, that he would draw, but was pleasingly disappointed; for he was not to be let off so. The well-breathed youth, hot-mettled, and flush with genial juices, was now fairly in for making me know my driver. As soon, then, as he had made a short pause, waking, as it were, out of the trance of pleasure (in which every sense seemed lost for a while, whilst, with his eyes shut and short quick breathings, he had yielded down his maiden tribute), he still kept his post, yet unsated with enjoyment, and solacing in these so new delights, till his stiffness, which had scarce perceptibly remitted, being thoroughly recovered to him, who had not once unsheathed, he proceeded afresh to cleave and open to himself an entire entry into me, which was not a little made easy to him by the balsamic injection with which he had just plentifully moistened the whole internals of the passage. Redoubling, then, the active energy of his thrusts, favoured by the fervid appetency of my motions, the soft oiled wards can no longer stand so effectual a picklock, but yield and open him an entrance: and now, with conspiring nature and my industry, strong to aid him, he pierces, penetrates, and at length, winning his way inch by inch, gets entirely in, and finally, a home-made thrust, sheathes it up to the guard; on the information of which, from the close jointure of our bodies (insomuch that the hair on both sides perfectly interweaved and encurled together), the eyes of the transported youth sparkled with more joyous fires, and all his looks and motions acknowledged excess of pleasure, which I now began to share, for I felt him in my very vitals! I was quite sick with delight! stirred beyond bearing with its furious agitations within me, and gorged and crammed even to a surfeit: thus I lay gasping, panting, under him, till his broken breathings, faultering accents, eyes twinkling with humid fires, lunges more furious, and an increased stiffness gave me to hail the approaches of the second period: – it came – and the sweet youth, overpowered with ecstasy, died away in my arms, melting in a flood that shot in genial warmth into the innermost recesses of my body, every conduit of which, dedicated to that pleasure, was on flow to mix with it. Thus we continued for some instants, lost, breathless, senseless of everything and in every part but those favourite ones of nature, in which all that we enjoyed of life and sensation was now totally concentred.

The following describes Fanny's initiation ceremony, watched by several others.

Now, whether my partner had exhausted all the modes of regaling the touch or sight, or whether he was now ungovernably wound up to strike, I know not; but briskly throwing off his clothes, the prodigious heat bred by a close room, a great fire, numerous candles, and even the inflammatory warmth of these scenes induced him to lay aside his shirt too, when his breeches, before loosened, now gave up their contents to view, and showed in front the enemy I had to engage with, stiffly bearing up the port of its head, unhooded and glowing red. Then I plainly saw what I had to trust to: it was one of those just true-sized instruments, of which the masters have a better command than the more unwieldy, inordinate sized ones are generally under. Straining me then close to his bosom, as he stood foreright against me, and applying to the obvious niche its peculiar idol, he aimed at inserting it, which, as I forwardly favoured, he effected at once by canting up my thighs over his naked hips, and making me receive every inch, and close home; so that stuck upon the pleasure pivot, and clinging round his neck, in which and in his hair I hid my face, burningly blushing with my present feeling as much as with shame, my bosom glued to his; he carried me once round the couch, on which he then, without quitting the middle-fastness, or dischannelling, laid me down, and began the pleasure grist. But so provokingly predisposed and primed as we were, by all the moving sights of the night, our imagination was too much heated not to melt us of the soonest: and accordingly, I no sooner felt the warm spray darted up my inwards from him, but I was punctually on flow, to share the momentary ecstasy; but I had yet greater reason to boast of our harmony: for finding that all the flames of desire were not yet quenched within me, but that rather, like wetted coals, I glowed the fiercer for this sprinkling, my hot-mettled spark, sympathizing with me, and loaded for a double fire, recontinued the sweet battery with undying vigour, greatly endeavoured to accommodate all my motions to his best advantage and delight; kisses, squeezes, tender murmurs, all came into play, till our joys, growing more turbulent and riotous, threw us into a fond disorder, and, as they raged to a point, bore us far from ourselves into an ocean of boundless pleasures, in which we both plunged together into a trans- port of taste. Now all the impressions of burning desire, from the lively scenes I had been spectatress of, ripened by the heat of this exercise, and collected to a head, throbbed and agitated me with insupportable irritations: I perfectly fevered and maddened with their excess. I did not now enjoy a calm of reason to perceive, but I ecstatically, indeed, felt the power of such rare and exquisite provocatives, as the examples of the night had proved towards thus exalting our pleasures: which, with great joy, I sensibly found my gallant shared in, by his nervous and home expressions of it: his eyes flashing eloquent flames, his action infuriated with the stings of it, all conspiring to raise my delight by assuring me of his. Lifted then to the utmost pitch of joy that human life can bear, undestroyed by excess, I touched that sweetly critical point, whence scarce prevented by the injection from my partner, I dissolved, and breaking out into a deep drawn sigh, sent my whole sensitive soul down to that passage where escape was denied it, by its being so deliciously plugged and choked up. Thus we lay a few blissful instants, overpowered, still, and languid; till, as the sense of pleasure stagnated, we recovered from our trance, and he slipped out of me, not, however, before he had protested his extreme satisfaction by the tenderest kiss and embrace, as well as by the most cordial expressions.

The company, who had stood round us in a profound silence, when all was over, helped me to hurry on my clothes in an instant, and complimented me on the sincere homage they could not escape observing had been done (as they termed it) to the sovereignty of my charms, in my receiving a double payment of tribute at one juncture. But my partner, now dressed again, signalized, above all, a fondness unbated by the circumstance of recent enjoyment; the girls too kissed and embraced me, assuring me that for that time, or indeed any other, unless I pleased, I was to go through no further trials, and that I was now consummately initiated, and one of them.

Fanny and Louisa find themselves alone in the house one day when a local youth calls on them with a basket of nosegays he is selling. The boy is tall and good looking but simple. Louisa decides to seduce him with Fanny's help, but soon realizes that she has bitten off rather more than she can chew.

Consequently, as soon as we came into Louisa's bed-chamber, while she was amusing him with picking out his nosegays, I undertook the lead, and began the attack.

As it was not then very material to keep much measures with a mere natural, I made presently very free with him, though at my first notion of meddling, his surprise and confusion made him receive my advances but awkwardly: nay, insomuch that he bashfully shied, and shied back a little; till encouraging him with my eyes, plucking him playfully by the hair, sleeking his cheeks, and forwarding my point by a number of little wantonnesses, I soon turned him familiar, and gave nature her sweetest alarm: so that aroused, and beginning to feel himself, we could, amidst all the innocent laugh and grin I have provoked him into, perceive the lightning fire in his eyes, and, diffusing over his cheeks, blend its glow with that of his blushes. The emotion in short of animal pleasure glared distinctly in the simpleton's countenance; yet, struck with the novelty of the scene, he did not know which way to look or move; but tame, passive, simpering, with his mouth half open in stupid rapture, stood and tractably suffered me to do what I pleased with him. His basket was dropped out of his hands, which Louisa took care of.

I had now, through more than one rent, discovered and felt his thighs, the skin of which seemed the smoother and fairer for the coarseness, and even dirt of his dress, as the teeth of Negroes seem the whiter for the surrounding black; and poor indeed of habit, poor of understanding, he was, however, abundantly rich in personal treasures, such as flesh, firm, plump, and replete with the beauties of youth, and robust well-knit limbs. My fingers too had now got within reach of the true, the genuine sensitive plant, which, instead of shrinking from the touch, joys to meet it, and swells and vegetates under it: mine pleasingly informed me that matters were so ripe for the discovery we meditated, that they were ready to break. A waistband that I unskewered, and a rag of a shirt that I removed, and which could not have covered a quarter of it, revealed the whole of the idiot's standard of distinction, erect, in full pride and display: but such a one! It was positively of so tremendous a size that, prepared as we were to see something extraordinary, it still, out of measure, surpassed our expectation, and astonished even me, who had not been used to trade in trifles. In fine, it might have answered very well the making a show of it; its enormous head seemed, in hue and size, not unlike a common sheep's heart; then you might have trolled dice securely along the broad back of the body of it; the length of it too was prodigious; then the rich appendage of the treasure-bag beneath, large in proportion, gathered and crisped up round in shallow furrows, helped to fill the eye, and complete the proof of his being a natural, not quite in vain; since it was full manifest that he inherited, and largely too, the prerogative of majesty which distinguishes that otherwise most unfortunate condition, and gives rise to the vulgar saying that "A fool's bauble is a lady's play-fellow." Not wholly without reason: for, generally speaking, it is in love as it is in war, where the longest weapon carries it. Nature, in short, had done so much for him in those parts that she perhaps held herself acquitted in doing so little for his head.

For my part, who had sincerely no intention to push the joke further than simply satisfying my curiosity with the sight of it alone, I was content, in spite of the temptation that stared me in the face, with having raised a maypole for another to hang a garland on: for, by this time, easily reading Louisa's desires in her wishful eyes, I acted the commodious part and made her, who sought no better sport, significant terms of encouragement to go through-stitch with her adventure; intimating too that I would stay and see fair play: in which, indeed, I had in view to humour a newborn curiosity, to observe what appearances active nature would put on in a natural, in the course of this her darling operation.

Louisa, whose appetite was up, and who, like the industrious bee, was it seems, not above gathering the sweets of so rare a flower, though she found it planted on a dunghill, was but too readily disposed to take the benefit of my cession. Urged then strongly by her own desires, and emboldened by me, she presently determined to risk a trial of parts with the idiot, who was by this time nobly inflamed for her purpose, by all the irritation we had used to put the principles of pleasure effectually into motion, and to wind up the springs of its organ to their supreme pitch; and it stood accordingly stiff and straining, ready to burst with the blood and spirits that swelled it – to a bulk! No! I shall never forget it.

Louisa then, taking and holding the fine handle that so invitingly offered itself, led the ductile youth by that master-tool of his, as she stepped backwards towards the bed; which he joyfully gave way to, under the incitations of instinct and palpably delivered up to the goad of desire.

Stopped then by the bed, she took the fall

she loved, and leaned to the most, gently backward upon it, still holding fast what she held, and taking care to give her clothes a convenient toss up, so that her thighs duly disclosed, and elevated, laid open all the outward prospect of the treasury of love: the rose-lipped overture presenting the cock-pit so fair that it was not in nature even for a natural to miss it. Nor did he: for Louisa, fully bent on grappling with it, and impatient of dalliance or delay, directed faithfully the point of the battering piece, and bounded up with a rage of so voracious an appetite, to meet and favour the thrust of insertion that the fierce activity on both sides effected it with such pain of distention, that Louisa cried out violently that she was hurt beyond bearing, that she was killed. But it was too late; the storm was up, and force was on her to give way to it, for now the man-machine, strongly worked upon by the sensual passion, felt so manfully his advantages and superiority, felt withal the sting of

pleasure so intolerable, that maddening with
it, his joys began to assume a character of
furiousness which made me tremble for the
too tender Louisa. He seemed, at this
juncture, greater than himself; his countenance, before so void of meaning, or expression, now grew big with the importance of
the act he was upon. In short, it was not now
that he was to be played the fool with. But,
what is pleasant enough, I myself was awed
into a sort of respect for him, by the comely
terrors his motions dressed him in: his eyes
shooting sparks of fire; his face glowing with
ardours that gave another life to it; his teeth
churning; his whole frame agitated with a
raging ungovernable impetuosity: all
sensibly betraying the formidable fierceness
with which the genial instinct acted upon
him. Butting then and goring all before him,
and mad and wild like an over-driven steer,
he ploughs up the tender furrow, all
insensible to Louisa's complaints; nothing
can stop, nothing can keep out a fury like

his: with which, having once got its head in, its blind rage soon made way for the rest, piercing, rending and breaking open all obstruction. The torn, split, wounded girl cries, struggles, invokes me to her rescue, and endeavours to get from under the young savage, or shake him off, but alas! In vain: her breath might as soon have stilled or stemmed a storm in winter, as all her strength have quelled his rough assault, or put him out of his course. And indeed, all her efforts and struggles were managed with such disorder that they served rather to entangle, and hold her faster in the twine of his boisterous arms; so that she was tied to the stake, and obliged to fight the match out, if she died for it. For his part, instinct-ridden as he was, the expressions of his animal passion, partaking something of ferocity, were rather worryings than kisses, intermixed with eager, ravenous love-bites on her cheeks and neck, the prints of which did not wear out for some days after. Poor

Louisa, however, bore up at length better than could have been expected; and though she suffered, and greatly too, yet, ever true to the good old cause, she suffered with pleasure and enjoyed her pain. And soon now, by dint of an enraged enforcement, the brute machine, driven like a whirlwind, made all smoke again, and wedging its way up to the utmost extremity, left her, in point of penetration, nothing to fear or to desire: and now

"Gorg'd with the dearest morsel of the earth,"

(Shakespeare)

Louisa lay, pleased to the heart, pleased to her utmost capacity of being so, with every fibre in those parts stretched almost to breaking, on a rack of joy, whilst the instrument of all this overfulness searched her senses with its sweet excess, till the pleasure gained upon her so, its point stung her so home, that catching at length the rage from her furious driver and sharing the riot of his wild rapture, she went wholly out of her mind into that favourite part of her body, the intenseness of which was so fervously filled, and employed: there alone she existed, all lost in those delirious transports, those ecstasies of the senses, which her winking eyes, the brightened vermilion of her lips and cheeks, and sighs of pleasure deeply fetched so pathetically expressed. In short, she was now as mere a machine, as much wrought on, and had her motions as little at her own command as the natural himself, who, thus broke in upon her, made her feel with a vengeance his tempestuous mettle he battered with; their active loins quivered again with the violence of their conflict, till the surge of pleasure, foaming and raging to a height, drew down the pearly shower that was to allay this hurricane. The purely sensitive idiot then first shed those tears of joy that attend its last moments, not without an agony of delight, and even almost a roar of rapture, as the gush escaped him; so sensible too was

Louisa that she kept him faithful company, going off, in consent, with the old symptoms: a delicious delirium, a tremulous convulsive shudder, and the critical dying "Oh!" And now, on his getting off, she lay pleasure-drenched, and re-gorging its essential sweets; but quite spent, and gasping for breath, without other sensation of life than in those exquisite vibrations that trembled yet on the strings of delight, which had been so ravishingly touched, and which nature had been too intensely stirred with, for the senses to be quickly at peace from.

THE AMOROUS EXPLOITS OF
A YOUNG RAKEHELL

~

Written by Guillaume Apollinaire (1880–
1918) with the express purpose of earning
much needed cash, *The Amorous Exploits of a
Young Rakehell* records the lustful exploits of
Roger, a young man on summer vacation
with his family at their chateau.
Apollinaire's more serious work includes
several collections of poetry and short
stories. A friend of many notable writers and
artists, including Picasso, Apollinaire
championed Cubism and was the originator
of the term "Surrealism."

from *The Amorous Exploits of a Young Rakehell*

~

When I awoke the next morning, I was lying on my back, a position which usually gives me an erection. Shortly thereafter I heard the sound of approaching footsteps. Wanting to play a joke on the bailiff's wife, I lifted my nightshirt, threw the blankets off me, and pretended to be asleep. But instead of the bailiff's wife, it was her sister-in-law, a woman of thirty-five or so, the age when a woman is at the height of sensuality.

Madame Muller was neither ugly nor beautiful. She was tall, had a strikingly good figure, a dark complexion and her hair, like her eyes, was pitch black. She seemed intelligent, and fully worthy of a bout with my John Thomas. And you could bet your last penny that she'd seen more than one such animal in her lifetime. So, I reasoned, why not let her see mine as well. I lay there motionless.

Madame Muller set the coffee on the night stand. Then seeing John Thomas standing stiffly at attention, she had a moment's hesitation. But she was a resolute woman, free from all false modesty. She spent several seconds gazing at me with apparent pleasure. Then she coughed discreetly to awaken me, and as I stretched my limbs in such a way as to give my prick an even more insolent air, she approached the bed, looked down for a second, then pulled the covers up and said: "Your coffee, Master Roger."

I opened my eyes, wished her good morning, and complimented her on how well she was looking, etc. Then I suddenly jumped out of the bed, seized her and assured her that she was the most beautiful woman in the whole chateau. She resisted weakly; slipping my hand beneath her skirts, I discovered a very hairy mound. Then I drove my finger into her cunt. As is the case with all sensual women, hers was dry, but my finger-work soon remedied that. Her clitoris was extremely hard.

"But what's come over you? Stop that! What would my husband say if he knew!"

"Mr Muller's in the chapel."

"Yes, I know. He does nothing but pray all day long. But stop that now, you're hurting me. My sister-in-law might come in. She's waiting for me. That's enough now! I'll come back tonight. My husband's leaving today for two or three days in the country. But now we're liable to be interrupted . . ."

And with that she took her leave. That evening, after having eaten a hearty dinner, I took some wine, ham and dessert back with me to my room. The chateau was soon asleep. Finally, after what seemed like hours, Madame Muller came in. My heart was beating like a triphammer. I embraced her, and gave her a French kiss, which she returned. I undressed quickly and showed

her my prick in a most presentable condition.

"Don't get so excited," she warned, "or
we'll waken the whole house and set the
tongues to wagging."

She bolted the door. I fastened her
mound in a tight grip, and found it slightly
swollen, and her clitoris extremely hard. I
stripped her down to her petticoat, and lifted
it high. Seeing her dressed you'd have taken
her for thin, but she wasn't in the least. In
fact if anything she was on the fleshy side.
Her dark pubic hair, I noticed, climbed all
the way up to her navel.

She must just have washed, for her Lady
Jane was odorless. Then I stripped her
completely and was amazed to find how firm
her breasts were. They were only moderately
large, and her nipples were set in a small field
of light brown hair.

Lifting her breasts, I saw that she also had
some short, fine black hairs underneath. Her
armpits were likewise covered with hair as

thick as a man's. What surprised me most as I examined her more closely, were her well raised buttocks, whose cheeks were set close together. Along her backbone ran a fine line of black hair, from top to bottom. The sight of all this healthy fleece caused John Thomas to harden even more.

I ripped off my nightshirt and straddled the lovely creature, whose rhythmic movements set my pickle slapping back and forth against her belly. We were in such a position that we could clearly see ourselves in the mirror. I led her toward the bed, where she sat down and said: "I know you want to see all of me." She raised her legs and displayed her hairy cunt right up to her pot-hole. I immediately set to tonguing her, and lingered at the task for quite some time. Her lips began to swell. When I went to insert my tool, she laughed and said: "Not like that. Get on the bed."

I asked her to please use the familiar "thou" form with me, and to allow me to do the same with her.

I got onto the bed. She climbed on top of me and I thus had her whole beautiful body before my eyes. She told me to play with her boobies. Then she grasped my prick, paraded it awhile against her love lips, and at the same time asked me to be sure not to come inside her. Then she suddenly shoved my tool in right up to the ball-bearings. She was riding me so strenuously that it was almost painful. Round about that time she came, and I could feel all the warmth of her cunt, hear her heaving sighs, and see her eyes roll back in her head.

Realizing that I was also on the point of coming, she got quickly to her feet. "Hold on a minute, young fellow, my lad," she said in a voice still trembling with emotion, "I know still another that'll satisfy you without making me pregnant." She turned round; her buttocks were now facing me. She bent down and took my prick in her mouth. I followed her example and began tonguing her love lips, lapping up the female love-juice which tasted like a raw egg. She stepped up the play of her tongue against my glans, and with one hand she tickled my balls and buttocks, while with the other she gripped my penis. I stiffened with pleasure. She thrust my prick as far in her mouth as possible. Her most secret parts were staring me full in the face. I seized her buttocks, and plunged my tongue into her pot-hole. I lost control of myself and ejaculated into her mouth.

RANDIANA

∼

According to the 1899 advertising literature for this novella, it was written by "an English gentleman of considerable wit, command of language, and an imagination of Rabelaisian order." The libidinous but anonymous narrator describes his epicurean experiences in this extract from *Randiana*, and in the subsequent piece taken from its sister novella, *The Adventures of Grace and Anna*.

from *Randiana*

∼

Gerty showed me to a room to prepare for dinner, and it was arranged we should have a real love seance after the servants had gone to bed. At dinner I saw Lady Fanny, who met me with a most fervent embrace, assuring me, with tears in her eyes, that I was the

source of the only happiness she had had in
her life (her son, now at Oxford).

All through dinner, and long after while
we sat on over dessert talking of old times, I
felt as proud as a barn-door cock with three
favourite hens, all glowing with love and
anxious for his attentions; the ardent
glances of lovely Mrs Leveson told too
plainly the force of her luscious recol-
lections, while Lady Fanny, who sat by my
side, every now and then caressed my prick
under the table, eliciting a slight throbbing
in response to her touches.

At length coffee was brought in, and the
servants told to go to bed.

"At last!" sighed our hostess, springing up
and throwing her arms around my neck, "I
have a chance to kiss the father of my boy;
what terrible restraint I have had to use
before the servants. Dear James, you belong
to us all, we all want the consolation of that
grand practitioner of yours; have which of us
you please first; there's no jealousy!"

"But darling loves, how can I do you all? I'm not the man I was some years ago!"

"Trust in Gerty's science, for she let us into the Pinero Balsam secret, and we have a little of it in the house for occasions when it might be wanted. It's very curious how you ruined the morals of both Fanny and myself, two such paragons of virtue as it were; we could never forget the lessons of love you taught us, and, now we are both widows, with dear Gerty here, we do enjoy ourselves on the quiet. Fanny's boy has me, and thinks it is an awfully delicious and secret liaison; my James returns the kindness to my love's mother; while dear abandoned Gerty is only satisfied sometimes by having both with her at once, yet none of them ever divulges their amour with Fanny and myself. And now, how is the dear jewel? You surely don't require the balsam to start with," she said taking out my staff of life, and kissing it rapturously. Lady Fanny did the same, and was followed by Gerty, whose ravishing manner of gamahuching me recalled so vividly my first seduction of her in the Temple. She would have racked me off, but I restrained myself, and requested them to peel to the buff, setting them the example, my cock never for a moment losing his fine erection.

Having placed an eider-down quilt and some pillows on the hearth-rug, they ranged themselves in front of me in all their naked glories, like the goddesses before Paris disputing for the apple. "Catch which you can," they exclaimed, laughing, and began capering around me.

I dashed towards Mrs Leveson, but tumbled over one of the pillows, getting my bottom most unmercifully slapped before I could recover myself. My blood tingled from head to foot. I was made to be into one of those luscious loving women, and in a moment or two caught and pulled down Fanny on top of me; the other two at once settled her, *à la* St George, and held my prick till she was fairly impaled on it. They then stretched themselves at full length on either side, kissing me ardently, while their busy fingers played with prick and balls, and the darling Fanny got quickly into her stride and rode me with the same fire and dash which characterized her first performance on her brother's bed in the Temple.

My hands were well employed frigging the creamy cunts of Mrs Leveson and Gerty — what a fuck, how my prick swelled in this agony of delight, as I shot the hot boiling sperm right up to Fanny's heart, and she deluged me in return with the essence of her life as she fell forward with a scream of delight. Her tightly nipping cunt held me enraptured by its loving contractions, but at the suggestion of Gerty she gently rolled herself aside and allowed me to mount the darling Leveson before I lost my stiffness.

What a deep-drawn sigh of delight my fresh fuckstress gave, as she heaved up her buttocks and felt my charger rush up to the very extremes of her burning sheath.

"Let me have the very uttermost bit of it! Keep him up to his work, Gerty, darling," she exclaimed excitedly, then gluing her lips to mine she seemed as if she would suck my very life away.

A smart, tingling, swish-swish on my rump now aroused me to the fact that both Fanny and Gerty had taken in hand the flagellation and, gradually putting more force in their cuts, they raised such a storm of lustful heat that I fucked dear Mrs Leveson till we both lost consciousness for a time in an ecstatic agony of bliss and when we recovered ourselves declared that no such exquisite sensations had ever before so completely overwhelmed either of us.

Such was the power of the rod to invigorate me that Gerty soon had her cunt as well stuffed as the others had been by my grand prick, which seemed to be bigger and stiffer than ever.

This loving seance was kept up into the small hours of the morning before I could think of tearing myself from their seductive delights; but I now often join this community of love in the Cromwell Road and no pen can by any possibility adequately describe the delights we manage to enjoy under the influence of the birch.

from *The Adventures of Grace and Anna*
~

I seized her by the hand and drew her down beside me and covered all of her lovely nakedness with kisses of fire, and my cock now in a state of pulsing hardness, I pushed her flat on her back and bestrode her, almost mad with pleasurable desire.

She opened her thighs wide and allowed me to lie within them, and presenting the head of my priapus at the entrance of her slit I thrust away at her, but was agreeably surprised to find that I could not even make the head of it enter; push as I might the natural dryness of my prong, together with the tightness of her orifice, made connection impossible.

"You-will-never-never-do-it!" she gasped, the breath driven out of her tender young body at the assaults I made upon her. "I – know it – I am too tight. It is a long time – a long time since I had it before!"

I determined that she was right in her surmise, and leaping to my feet I pulled the bell cord for Joseph and stood surveying her as she lay naked on the floor.

"What are you going to do?" she asked, looking up at me, and making as if to rise to her feet, but I again gently pushed her back on her back.

"I am ringing for Joseph," I explained, "and will secure some cold cream to ease the situation. You need not worry at his entrance, as he is to have you, too, and it will be a pleasant introduction for him."

At this instant Joseph discreetly knocked at the door and I admitted him and made known my wants in this particular direction.

He cast a glance at the girl on the floor and she turned her face on the cushions in shame; from the opened front of his pants I knew that he had been consoling Anna; he went and fetched a jar of the desired unguent.

Placing it on the cushion beside us, I again mounted the form of the prostrate girl, and anointing the head of my staff liberally, I took her again in my arms and again essayed the ravishment of her sexual charms. This time I succeeded in wedging the head within the tightly-closed lips, and settling down full upon her, I pushed forward with my loins and soon had a full inch of my throbbing rod impaled in her vitals.

"O-o-o-o-o-h-h-h," she murmured, thrashing about on the cushions and placing her hands against my chest as though to push me from her, "you are h-u-r-t-i-n-g me! Oh, oh, oh, that is too – too big! Take it out a minute! Just a minute! It stretches me too much! You are . . . wait! Wait!"

But I had gained my point and was in no

mood to relinquish it, and passing my hands behind her naked and bouncing posteriors I poised myself high upon her and with one drive sheathed half of the entire length of my dart into its clinging and trembling cove, and she gave a wild scream of pain and fell back trembling and senseless in my arms.

That one cruel plunge must have hurt her, but now seeing that she was insensible I made the most of the opportunity, and with a few more drives soon was in her cove to the hilt and then lay panting upon her till nature saw fit to restore her to her senses.

I knew that the cry must have startled Anna, but depended upon Joseph and the soothing presence of his kidney tosser to secure me from interruption, and the door being locked, waited with patience for her return to her senses.

She soon began to thrash about, and opening her eyes, moved her loins about, and the first pain of the entrance over, I began a slow weaving, rhythmic motion on her body, allowing my prong to glide in and out of the heated moistness of her glove-like membranes.

"Oh, oh, oh," she cried, "you are cruel, cruel indeed! Why could you not be easier with me?"

Then, pain giving way to more passionate sensations, she allowed her bare arms to steal tightly around my neck and her loins gave me back thrust for thrust and her lips met mine in a clinging embrace and we melted into one, a moving rhythm of lust, and our breath came in pants and bursts as I held her close to me.

"Oh, oh, oh-h-h-h-h-h-h-h-h-h!" she signed, thrusting upwards with all her might to meet the descending charger, "oh, oh, o-h-h, there . . . t-h-e-r-e!!!" as her slit opened and closed on my staff with lightning-like loving strokes.

"T-h-e-r-e, that, t-h-a-t is it! Oh, ohohohohoh o-o-o-o-o, I'm coming! O-h-h-h, lover darling, that is s-o-o-o-n-i-c-e!"

And her hot flow bathed and sprayed my swelling charger.

Again and again this delightful compression of her tight slit took place, and each time she vented a shower of girlish dew upon me, and feeling that I, also, was about to spend I took her firmly in my arms and whispered in her ear, "Here, here! Here is the child that you fear! I will spout into your womb a living, pulsing life! There, there, there," as I exploded in her, "that is the first fruit of your marriage! Take it and rear it as a gift from me!" And I shot and bubbled in great spurts into her womb the largest charge that I could ever recall, and driving my prong far up into her, sought the more firmly to embed it within the most secret confines of her being.

She, at the same instant, gave down another charge, and we then lay melting in each other's arms, relaxed and breathless on the cushions.

SADOPAIDEIA

~

No book of erotica would be complete without a piece on flagellation, and this archetypal sub rosa novel provides just such an example, albeit relatively innocuous in content. Published anonymously (although now thought to be the work of J. P. Kirkwood), in 1907, *Sadopaideia* is an account of an Oxford student's initiation into the art of both subservience and dominance under the instruction of the beautiful Muriel Harcourt and Juliette, her "maid."

from *Sadopaideia*

~

Now I knew nothing at that time of flagellation. I had heard of old men needing the birch to excite them, but beyond that I knew nothing. So I said, "Punish me in any way you like, only let me stay and prove to you how sorry I am and how I love you."

"Very well," she said, "get behind that screen," pointing to a large Chinese screen that stood in the corner. I obeyed and she rang the bell.

Juliette appeared. "Take the tea things away and bring me my leather case."

I thought I heard a chuckle from Juliette but was not sure. After a little while I heard her come in again and whisper something to her mistress. "Yes, very," replied the latter. Then came more whisperings and I heard Mrs Harcourt say, "Oh, did he? Well, we shall see."

She then told me to come out, and I obeyed. I must have made rather a ridiculous figure, as my trousers were still down. Mrs Harcourt, however, did not seem to show any disposition to laugh. In fact, she looked very angry indeed. I went towards her, but she stopped me with a gesture and said, "You promise to do everything I tell you."

"Anything," I said.

"Very well. Turn your back to me and put your hands behind you."

I obeyed.

She opened the case and took something out, I could not see what, and then she came to me. I felt something cold touch my wrists and heard a snap. I tried to move my arms and to my surprise I found I could not. She had, in a moment, very deftly handcuffed me. I was too surprised to speak. "Now kneel down," she said.

"What for?" said I.

"You promised to do everything I told you," she repeated.

I knelt down awkwardly enough, with my hands fastened behind, just in front of the big couch. Then Mrs Harcourt took a large handkerchief and blindfolded me. I didn't like the look of things at all, but said nothing.

"Now," said Mrs Harcourt to me as I knelt

there helpless, "you have been a very rude and dirty boy and you must be punished. Are you sorry?"

I was just about to answer then "whish," something whistled through the air and I felt as if a hundred needles were pricking my bottom. I could not help an involuntary cry.

I heard a sigh of pleasure, and felt a hand on my neck, pressing me forward on to the couch.

"Are you sorry, eh?" she repeated, and again came the smart cut across my bottom.

I had never been birched in my life. At school a tanning cane was used, but I could easily guess what was the weapon she was using.

"Will you speak? Are you sorry?" she repeated, and again the rod descended. I tried to escape but my hands being tied hampered me, and though I could and did kick lustily, her hand on my neck managed to prevent me escaping altogether.

"Keep still," she said, "or I shall get

Juliette to help me. Are you sorry?" At that moment in one of my struggles the birch just caught my balls, causing excruciating pain.

"Yes, oh yes," I shouted.

"Will you ever do it again?" – whish – whish.

"No."

"What was it you did? Confess your fault."

Silence on my part. I felt too angry and ashamed to say.

"Will you confess?" – whish – whish – whish.

"Oh yes, I will."

"Well, what was it?"

"I came in your mouth."

"And what else?" – whish – "What else?"

"I don't know."

"Didn't you say you thought I wanted it?"

"Yes."

"Well, confess then."

"I said I thought you wanted it."

"Ah!" and again the blows fell all over my bottom.

The burning pain got worse and I struggled and wriggled and kicked so that I at last got away from her, managed to rub the handkerchief away from my eyes and swung round and looked at her.

I never saw such a change in a woman. If she was pretty before, she was lovely now. Her eyes were shining, her cheeks were flushed, the exertion of plying the rod had caused one shoulder strap of her chemise to break and one breast was just exposed.

I looked at her with adoring eyes. I couldn't help it. Angry and hurt as I was in my dignity and elsewhere, I could not but feel admiration and — yes, even affection. She met my eyes.

"Well," she said, "why have you turned round? I haven't finished yet."

"Isn't that enough?" I said. "I've said I'm sorry and confessed my fault."

"Haven't you any other faults to confess?"

"No!"

She rang the bell.

I exclaimed, "You're surely not going to let anyone see me like this?"

She made no reply and the door opened and Juliette appeared.

"Juliette, come here," she said. "You see this gentleman here; now repeat before him the accusation you whispered to me just now."

Juliette looked at me with a malicious smile (I remembered that smile) and said, "When I was hanging the gentleman's hat up in the hall, he offered to help me, and then he kissed me and felt my breast and tried to feel my pussy through my skirt."

"You little cat," I said.

"Is that true?" said Mrs Harcourt. "Answer me," and the birch fell across my thighs as I lay twisted on the couch. It flicked up my shirt-tail and exposed John Thomas to the salacious gaze of Juliette. I was too ashamed to speak.

"Will you answer me!" and again and again came the cutting strokes, one of them just catching poor John Thomas nicely.

"Well, if I did, she did as much to me," I muttered.

"Oh, indeed," said Mrs Harcourt, as Juliette darted a vicious look at me. "Well, we can investigate that later. Get the bands, Juliette."

Juliette went to the case and produced a long band of webbing-working on a loop and, before I knew what she was about, had slipped it round my ankles and drawn it tight. Now I was indeed helpless.

"Now Juliette," said her mistress, "as it was you who were insulted, it is only fair for you to punish him."

They turned me over face downwards and turned up my shirt.

"Oh, he's had some already, I see," said the maid.

"Yes, a little," said the mistress. "He can do with some more."

"How many?" said Juliette, taking up the birch.

"We'll see."

Then the pain began again. Blow after blow, cut after cut, until my poor bottom felt as if it was on fire. I wriggled as much as I could but couldn't do much. My motions, however, must have pleased Mrs Harcourt, for she said, "Wait a moment, Juliette, we mustn't be too hard. He shall have some pleasure as well as pain."

She got round to the other side of the couch, raised my head, which was buried in the cushions, and, bending down, whispered to me, "He's a naughty boy, but I love him, so he can kiss me if he likes."

She then pulled up her clothes and presented her pussy backwards to me which I could just reach with my tongue.

"Now Juliette," she said, "not too hard, and cleverly." I did not feel at all anxious to justify her wishes, but to my surprise the birch fell now in quite a different way. Instead of the slashing cuts which had made me writhe and smart, the blows simply warmed my bottom.

Of course now and then it touched an extra sore place and made me flinch, but for the most part the twigs seemed to caress, and the tips of them, curling in between the cheeks, gave me a delightful sensation, and I felt John Thomas answering in a way that surprised me. I forgot my resentment against Mrs Harcourt and my tongue roamed about her lovely pussy and even went higher and caressed the other "fair demesnes that there adjacent lay" and which presented themselves to my eyes, a proceeding which evidently pleased her, for she opened and shut the cheeks of her bottom, and at last with a quick side twist and a final plunge she forced her pussy right against my mouth, and murmuring, "That will do Juliette," she smothered my mouth and chin with her delicious cream.

She then got up and with Juliette's aid undid my bonds. I lay still, too excited to move. I felt her arm round my neck, while her other caressed my bottom. "Poor boy," she said, "did it hurt very much?"

I turned round and kissed her. I couldn't help it. All my rage and feeling of insult seemed to have disappeared. "That's right," she said, nestling close to me. "So the whipping did him good! It didn't go on too long though, I hope," she added, quickly pulling up my shirt and looking at my John Thomas, who by this time, after the last part of the birching, was nearly bursting. "No, that's all right. Come to me, darling."

"But Juliette!" I said.

"Oh, never mind her . . . Still, perhaps she had better go," she added with a peculiar look. "Juliette, you can go, I shall want you in a quarter of an hour.

Juliette looked very disappointed, but had to go.

"Now, darling," said her mistress, "come to me and love me, and say you forgive your cruel mistress for hurting you."

She unfastened the band of her petticoat and let it fall. Then she stepped out of it. Her teagown was wide open, and, as I have said, one shoulder of her chemise had broken, so she was practically naked to the waist.

She went to the chair again and sat down right on the edge, lying right back so that her bottom jutted just over the edge. I knelt before her and found her pussy was just at the right height for John Thomas.

Her legs went over my shoulders and I gently placed him in position and began work.

I have never known such an expert in the art of love. Every conceivable motion and twist of her body she used. Her eyes flickered with passion, her lips drew my tongue right into her mouth, while her hands led mine all over her body. She murmured words of love and desire, mingled with pity for my poor bottom. At last she said, "He was a very naughty boy, but it was a shame to cut him so badly. Never mind, someday perhaps he will have a chance to retaliate." Then the final paroxysm came on and we were both dumb.

My motions, which had been slow at first, grew quicker. She plunged and writhed, twisting her legs round my neck and raising her bottom to meet my strokes, until at last, with a half-sob, half-groan, her legs fell down from my shoulders and I poured into her eager womb a deluge of my love.

MY SECRET LIFE

~

Much studied and discussed by erotologists, *My Secret Life* was written by an upper middle-class gentleman whose pen name was "Walter." Little is known about him other than that he was a businessman born into a middle-class family around 1820 and died about 1894. More brutal and selfish in tone than most of the books extracted here, it is nevertheless the most factual sexual autobiography in existence, comprising eleven volumes (amounting to over four thousand pages), and describing the life of a man who purportedly had sex with over twelve hundred women.

from *My Secret Life*

❧

In a fortnight I had often kissed Loo, and pinched her bum till she said it was blue. I told her I should like to sleep with her, for I loved her. This was on the first night she got out for a walk at dusk. I had heard her aunt say she'd keep a tight hand on her, and I found Loo was fast almost to a gallop. We walked and sat down on a beach seat. "How can you love me? You're married."

"I never said I wasn't, but I hate her and do nothing to her, and love you."

"Oh, gammon!" she replied. I had now a little changed my opinion about the girl. She wanted to know the meaning of my "doing nothing", was free in manner, and any delicate smut which I began using she answered frankly to. "Oh! I knows what you means well enough, but don't you go on like that." I concluded that she had been brought up with coarse people who spoke of all their wants and acts openly, so that the girl saw no harm in such things. She had only been with her aunt that summer. She told me of her relatives, and where they lived in Northumberland. There was a large family, but that was all I could get out of her. "Yer don't want to call on 'em," she said laughing.

All was soon finished with the servant. One morning I waited indoors in hopes of getting at Loo, and spied the servant as she brought a slop pail to the closet close to the bedroom.

When she came out I asked her into that room, which I had never entered before. "Come here, I've something particular to tell you."

Reluctantly she came in, then I kissed, and gradually getting to the unchaste, got my hand on her cunt. "Be quiet, Mrs Jones will be up to see if all's right."

"No, she's out. Oh! What lovely thighs."

"Oh, leave off, I'll tell Mrs Jones, I will."

I desisted for a moment, but only to pull

out my prick. I pushed her against the bedside, and got my fingers on to her cunt again. "Let me have you." I fucked her standing.

After, she took the money without a word, and pushed me off when I tried to kiss her, and I never got at her again.

I had doubted Betsy, and though she was going to sell me about the virginity, spite of her protestations, and spite of my telling her that if not satisfied, I would only give her the price of a fuck of herself, and a little present to the girl: and knowing the room and the way the furniture was placed, and where the gas was, this now occurred to me again. I had to prevent my being cheated, and to get a good look, brought a candle with me which I now lighted, and stood by the side of the bed, Betsy close to me. I took one of the girl's legs, Betsy the other. "Open your thighs and let him look, you said you would – you

promised me you would — there's a darling,"
said she.

The girl's legs opened wide. I gave Betsy
the candle, and with the vacant hand pulled
open wide the lips of the little cunt, which
was of a delicate pink, with the slightest
signs of dark hair just on the mons. Excited
as I was, and with a prick throbbing as if it
would burst, or spend without a touch, I saw
that the cunt had never had anything larger
than a finger up it. With an impulse I have
always had with hairless cunts, I put my
mouth to it, and gave it a little lick. Such a
mouthful of saliva came, and ran out of my
mouth at once. The girl struggled as she felt
my tongue, and closed her thighs on my
head. The spittle had covered her cunt. I
threw off my shirt, pushed Molly straight on
the bed, got on it by the side of her, and
Betsy got on the other side.

But she would not let me mount her. In
vain Betsy coaxed and bullied by turns. "No,
no," — she had altered her mind. She was

frightened – it would hurt, that great thing would hurt her, it would make her bleed. Then she burst into tears and cried. I desisted, Betsy quieted her, for fear of the people of the house, and when she had done she spoke to her in a subdued voice as nearly possible thus.

"You bloody little fool. I had pricks up me twice as big as that, and longer than his, before I was your age – don't I get a living by fucking? Don't I get silk stockings and dresses by fucking? How are you going to live? Who's going to keep you, I want to know? What did you come here for? Didn't you say you'd like to be fucked if it was nicer than frigging yourself?"

The girl made no reply and was confused and shaking. "All right, you may go, and you may get home as you can." Saying that, she jumped off the bed and rolled up in a bundle the girl's chemise and petticoat, which were quite new. "You shan't have the things I've given you, damned if you shall." Then she came to the bed, violently pulled off from the girl both boots and stockings, and rolled up the stockings with the petticoat. "Now you may go – put on your dress and your boots, and go, you're not wanted here, my friend and I will stop all night."

The girl looked scared out of her senses. "Don't Betsy, where am I to go to?" "Go to Hell and buggery, go and shit yourself, I don't care a bloody fart where you go to."

The girl blubbered and sobbed out: "I will then, I will let him."

"Hold your snivelling, and don't make that noise. Let him do it to you, if you don't, go and you know what."

I got on to the bed again. So did Betsy, who helped the girl to her old place. Again the girl said she should be hurt and refused. "You do it Betsy, with him, you let him do it."

"Lord," said Betsy, who had recovered her temper, "he may fuck me till his spunk come up into my mouth if he likes – show her how to do it – let's have a fuck my dear," and she winked at me. "Show her how it's done, and then she will let you, won't you Molly?" Molly made no reply.

I knelt between Betsy's legs naked, with prick stiff, dropped on to her, and put my prick up her. "There, feel, Molly." She took hold of the girl's hand and guided it between our bellies – "Feel, his prick's right up – turn a little on the side," said she to me. We did, keeping copulated. When her arse was a little turned towards Molly, she threw one thigh high up over my hips so that the girl could see the prick as it lay squeezed into Betsy's cunt. "Look under, look Molly – look there, nothing but his balls to see, is there?" The girl put her head down, and curious, touched my balls. "Oh fuck, fuck, isn't it lovely my darling," said Betsy.

We turned flat again and Betsy began fucking and heaving in earnest. She thought she was going to have the treat for she wanted it. But I slipped my prick out of her cunt, tho I kept on ramming and driving, as if I was going to fuck her backside up to her blade bones. "Sham," I whispered. Betsy, tho disappointed, took the hint, and we heaved and pushed together, my prick now outside her, and at length screaming out, "Fuck – cunt – Oh lovely – ah my spunk's coming – oh push hard dear. We both shammed ecstatic pleasure and sunk quietly down, whilst the lass sitting up naked on the bed by our side looked at us all the while intently.

"Let him do it to you," said Betsy, again coaxing and threatening Molly. My prick had drooped, just as the girl at last allowed me to get between her thighs, but it sprung up stiff directly I dropped on to her. I worked cunningly, rubbing the tip just outside till I had lodged it. She trembled. I pressed her, and gave a tremendous thrust, and was on the right road. "Oho – hah – ar," she screamed. "You hurt – get off – I won't let you – har." She screeched loudly, and struggled violently. "Hish, you damned howling little bitch," said Betsy, pushing a pillow right over the girl's head. I pressed my head on the pillow, the girl's head was hidden from me, but I could hear her cry. I had not got up her, was funky about the noise we were making, but in the excitement thought only of my work. "Hish, they will hear," were the last words I heard Betsy say. Then I felt my sperm was coming and with a violent effort, and grasping the fat little buttocks like a vice — my prick went up her, leaving my sperm all the way up as I entered. I felt the tightening of her hymen round my prick, as it went through it was a cunt-splitting thrust.

It was all over in a minute. Then, "Oh, don't," I heard in muffled tones. "Have you done her?" said Betsy. "Y — hes — y- hes." She pulled away the pillow, and there I lay with the little naked one palpitating, but quiet in my arms, my prick up to its roots in her. I kept it there, tho it was shrinking, but I kept on gently thrusting, just enough to keep it half stiff. Then I partially withdrew it, the girl winced and murmured, "Oh, take it out, you do hurt." That stiffened me quite. "I am fucking again. I shall spend again," I said to Betsy, who turned on her side to see better, and in a few minutes of exquisitely prolonged pleasures, I spermatized again the little virgin quim.

PARISIAN FROLICS

~

Originally written as four independent short stories, *Parisian Frolics* exemplifies the decadence of Paris during La Belle Epoque. Written by Adolphe Belot (1829–90) and first published as a collection in 1906, the stories describe the licentious exploits of the wealthy Henri R, who spends much of his time in the "pleasure houses" of the period.

from *Parisian Frolics*

~

Mme de Liancourt slowly slipped off her position and then gave her pupil kiss after kiss of approbation and satisfaction.

"Darling! Your face is all wet with what you have drawn out of me! And I've drunk you. Use my handkerchief. How flushed and red you are! Now, wasn't that good?"

"Oh, yes. Much better than I could have believed!"

Was it not now time for me to put in an appearance? But what could I do with two women whose lust had been thus satiated! Nevertheless, I decided to show myself and opened the door, regretting that I had delayed so long!

Two piercing cries saluted me! Martha leaped on her piled-up garments and covered herself as best she could with the first she could snatch, then hid herself behind the bed curtains. Mme de Liancourt caught up a velvet mantle trimmed with fur and threw it hastily around her, but it reached only to her fleshy buttocks and did not even cover the fur of her belly.

"What do you mean, sir," she exclaimed with a fine pretence of anger and outraged modesty. "What do you mean by thus rushing into a lady's room without first knocking? It is a piece of the greatest impertinence! You are a mannerless brute!"

"Madame, I humbly and earnestly beg your pardon for having surprised you in this way," I replied, suppressing as best I could the desire to laugh. "But I came in trusting in your promise to give the kind refuge to this lady and myself!"

"Yes – but Madame has been waiting for you for some time now; is this your idea of the proper way of keeping an appointment? But I will abide by my promise; you can have my room and my bed. Only be prudent! I know your secrets now and if I choose I can be nasty!" She winked at me out of the corner of her eye as if to qualify her menace, then walked past me towards her dressing-room.

"Take care about the sheets!" she added with a meaningfully wicked smile.

I watched as she walked, her lovely plump and round bottom quivering and waggling with every step. I would dearly have liked to have put myself into her! But I went and dragged Martha out of her hiding place.

"What makes you so red, dear?"

"I've been laughing! Madame has been telling me the funniest stories . . ."

"You look simply charming in that dressing gown – but don't fasten it up, it's quite unnecessary!"

"Oh . . . very well. But wait a minute. Don't look!"

She disappeared into the lavatory, and while she was engaged in clearing away all traces of her recent pranks, I undressed myself, then when she reappeared, I took her in my arms and carried her to the bed on which I gently laid her. Her desires, which I had feared were by now dormant, were quickly restored to life again, having another promise of satisfaction in a different way! Her modesty after so rude an experience had become less troublesome and I did not meet with any marked resistance on her part, when after bestowing a thousand kisses all over her body, I did to her what Mme de Liancourt had so sweetly inaugurated — the deliciousness of which she now fully appreciated as with her two little hands she pressed my face against her slit so as not to lose a single movement of my tongue!

I thought of Mme de Liancourt and wished she could see us now! But she did even better than that; she stood stark naked by the side of the bed, and while I was busy between Martha's thighs, she kissed her lips and squeezed her breasts — while the former, having within her reach her friend's thighs, slipped her hand between them and let it disappear under the plentiful cluster of curling hairs without interrupting my ministrations.

Excited, inflamed, burning with hot desire, I rose to throw myself on Martha and quench in her the fire that was raging in my veins! But at that moment Mme de Liancourt carried her hand to the lowest point of my belly and seized the object she found there in a state of furious erection!

"Look, Martha!" she exclaimed. "Have you ever seen it before? Isn't it splendid? See, how stiff it is – that's in honour of you, my dear! Oh, I must . . . I can't help it . . ."

I was then kneeling on the bed. With a single quick movement she seated herself with her head at the required height, then covered with hot kisses my member which she found just on a level with her lips. She kissed and rekissed the glans, the hairs, the testicles, murmuring endearments; then she took my prick into her mouth and sucked it madly in front of Martha, who was watching her in utter astonishment!

"Now, Martha, you take it – it's your turn. Suck it. Do as I did!"

"I don't know how to! It's so big!"

Now redder than fire, she approached it, kissed the tip and tried for some time in vain to take it into her mouth – when all of a sudden it slipped in, as if in spite of her, completely filling her mouth. And she then proceeded to suck me. Oh, my raptures! It was Martha! Martha herself that was sucking me! It was not with the lascivious skill of Mme de Liancourt, but her inexperience itself gave to her caress a special and indescribable spice of pleasure.

Finally I put Martha flat on her back. I let myself fall between her arms and legs and shoved my prick into her burning cunt – tasting delights hitherto unknown – divine, delirious! Already I could see Martha's eyes slowly turning upwards and half closing, indicating her approaching ecstasy – when Mme de Liancourt, no doubt jealous of our transports, put herself astride across Martha's face, blindly seeking for her cunt a further caress which it was impossible to refuse to her! Being thus suddenly driven away from Martha's lips and tongue, I transferred my kisses to the two luscious globes of flesh which I had at my mouth's command, kissing, nibbling and playfully biting them in spite of their squirming and constant agitation!

But everything must end. We three spent simultaneously! The blissfull ejaculations of sperm calmed us! One by one, we came to our senses and rose to purify and refresh ourselves.

EROTIC VERSE

It is difficult to define erotic verse, as love, and particularly sexual love, has been the source and theme of poetry throughout history. In some poems the erotic imagery is so subtle that one wonders if the poet meant it to be erotic at all; in others there is no doubt whatsoever, as in the wonderful lines from Swinburne's "Love and Sleep," excerpted here. The following collection ranges from simple love poems to bawdy rhymes and begins with a selection of Priapeia.

PRIAPEIA

~

Priapeia is the word given to the Latin epigrams inscribed on the statues of Priapus, the god of fertility. These short, witty poems, only relatively recently translated by Leonard Smithers and Sir Richard Burton, are thought to have been written by some of the great Roman poets such as Juvenal, Catullus and Martial, and were often used to deter thieves or trespassers.

Why laugh such laughter, O most silly maid?
My form Praxiteles nor Scopas hewed;
To me no Phidian handwork finish gave;
But me a bailiff hacked from shapeless log,
And quoth my maker, "Thou Priapus be!"
Yet on me gazing forthright gigglest thou
And holdest funny matter to deride
The pillar perking from the groin of me.

(Note: Praxiteles produced a famous statue of Venus; Scopas was a sculptor in marble, Phidias a sculptor in ivory.)

Though I be wooden Priapus (as thou see'st),
With wooden sickle and a prickle of wood,
Yet will I seize thee, girl! and hold thee seized
And *This*, however gross, withouten fraud
Stiffer than lyre-string or than twisted rope
I'll thrust and bury to thy seventh rib.

Thou, of unrighteous thought, that hardly
    canst
Refrain from robbing this my garden-plot,
With foot-long fascinum shalt bulghar'd be:
Yet if so mighty grievous punishment
Profit thee naught, at higher stead I'll strike.

(Translation: Anyone robbing my garden will be
sodomized by my twelve-inch phallus, and if that's not
enough of a deterrent, I will use your mouth instead!)

What hast thou, meddling watch, with me to
    do?
Why baulk the robber who to me would
    come?
Let him draw nigh: the laxer shall he go.

from *De Rerum Natura, Book IV*

~

Thus, therefore, he who feels the fiery dart
Of strong desire transfix his amorous heart,
Whether some beauteous boy's alluring face
Or lovelier maid with unresisted grace
From her each part the winged arrow sends,
From whence he first was struck, he thither
   tends.
Restless he roams, impatient to be freed
And eager to inject the sprightly seed.
For fierce desire does all his mind employ,
And ardent love assures approaching joy.

Lucretius (c. 99–c. 55 BC)
Translated by John Dryden

To a Mistress

~

My woman says she'll never be the lover of
any man, or even Jove himself. She says so.

What a woman says to an eager lover, write in
the water, write in the rushing waves.

Catullus (c. 84–c. 54 BC)

from *The Sixth Satire*

～

Hear what Claudius suffered: When his wife
    knew he was asleep,
This imperial harlot, without a trace of
    shame, would creep
From the marriage bed in the palace to seek
    the pallet of lust
That she preferred. Attired in a night-cloak,
    she left with just
One maid; and, with her black hair disguised
    by a blond wig served
In a brothel in which an empty crib was
    always reserved
For her, with bedclothes reeking still from
    the last encounter.
There she stood in the door, waiting for men

to mount her,
Naked, with nipples gold-tipped, with
    Lycisca as business name,
And flaunted the womb from which you, O
    noble Britannicus, came.
She welcomed all comers warmly, and always
    demanded her pay.
At dawn, when the bawd dismissed his girls,
    she chose to stay,
The last to close her stall; and still with fire
    in her womb,
Erect like a man in her heat, she sadly left
    the room,
Exhausted by dozens of men, but still not
    satisfied.
Then sooty from smoke of lamps, her sweat-
    smeared cheeks now dried,
She brought to the palace bed a perfect
    whorehouse stench.
Why talk of love potions, spells, or poisons
    brewed to quench
A stepson's life? These sex-mad, sex-driven
    women don't wince

At doing the foulest crimes; and lust is the
     least of their sins.

Juvenal (AD 59–130)
Translated by Hubert Creekmore

The Faerie Queene

~

And her two lilly paps aloft display'd
And all, that might his melting heart entise
To her delights, she unto him betray'd:
The rest hid underneath, him more desirous
     made.

Edmund Spenser (1552–99)

from *Antony and Cleopatra*

~

Age cannot wither her, not custom stale
Her infinite variety. Other women cloy

The appetites they feed; but she makes
  hungry
Where she most satisfies.

William Shakespeare (1564–1616)

Sonnet to Pleasure

∼

Licence my roving hands, and let them go,
Before, behind, between, above, below.
O my America, my new-found-land,
My kingdom, safest when one man man'd.

John Donne (1572–1631)

The Debauchee

∼

I rise at eleven, I dine about two,
I get drunk before sev'n; and the next thing I
  do,
I send for my whore, when for fear of a clap,

I spend in her hand, and I spew in her lap;

Then we quarrel and scold, 'till I fall fast asleep,

When the bitch, growing bold, to my pocket does creep;

Then slily she leaves me, and, to revenge the affront,

At once she bereaves me of money and cunt.

If by chance then I wake, hot-headed and drunk,

What a coil do I make for the loss of my punk?

I storm and I roar, and I fall in a rage,

And missing my whore, I bugger my page.

Then, crop-sick all morning, I rail at my men,

And in bed I lie yawning 'till eleven again.

John Wilmot, Earl of Rochester (1648–80)

from *A New Song of New Similes*

~

Pert as a pear-monger I'd be
If Molly were but kind;
Cool as a cucumber could see
The rest of womankind.

Like a stuck pig I gaping stare,
And eye her o'er and o'er;
Lean as a rake with sighs and care,
Sleek as a mouse before.

Hard is her heart as flint or stone,
She laughs to see me pale;
And merry as a grig is grown,
And brisk as bottled ale.

Straight as a leg her shape appears;
O were we join'd together!
My heart would be scot-free from cares,
And lighter than a feather.

As soft as pap her kisses are,
Methinks I taste them yet;

Brown as a berry is her hair,
Her eyes as black as jet.

Brisk as a body-louse she trips,
Clean as a penny drest;
Sweet as a rose her breath and lips,
Round as the globe her breast.

Full as an egg was I with glee;
And happy as a King.
Good Lord! how all men envy'd me!
She lov'd like anything!

John Gay (1685–1732)

A Valentine

～

What shall I send my sweet today,
When all the woods atune in love?
And I would show the lark and dove,
That I can love as well as they.

I'll send a locket full of hair, –
But no, for it might chance to lie

Too near her heart, and I should die
Of love's sweet envy to be there.

A violet is sweet to give, –
Ah, stay! She'd touch it with her lips,
And, after such complete eclipse,
How could my soul consent to live?

I'll send a kiss, for that would be
The quickest sent, the lightest borne,
And well I know tomorrow morn
She'll send it back again to me.

Go, happy winds; ah, do not stay,
Enamoured of my lady's cheek,
But hasten home, and I'll bespeak
Your services another day!

Matilda Betham-Edwards (1777–1852)

No, Never Think

~

No, never think, my dear, that in my heart I
 treasure
The tumult of the blood, the frenzied gusts
 of pleasure,
Those groans of hers, those shrieks: a young
 Bacchante's cries,
When writhing like a snake in my embrace
 she lies,
And wounding kiss and touch, urgent and
 hot, engender
The final shudderings that consummate
 surrender.
How sweeter far are you, my meek, my quiet
 one,
By what tormenting bliss is my whole soul
 undone
When, after I have long and eagerly been
 pleading,
With bashful graciousness to my deep need
 conceding,

You give yourself to me, but shyly, turned
    away,
To all my ardors cold, scarce heeding what I
    say,
Responding, growing warm, oh, in how slow
    a fashion,
To share, unwilling, yet to share at last my
    passion!

Alexander Pushkin (1799–1837)
Translated by Babette Deutsch

from *In Memoriam*

Fair ship, that from the Italian shore
Sailest the placid ocean-plains
With my lost Arthur's loved remains
Spread thy full wings, and waft him o'er

So draw him home to those that mourn
In vain; a favourable speed
Ruffle thy mirrored mast, and lead
Through prosperous floods his holy urn.

All night no ruder air perplex
Thy sliding keel, till Phosphor, bright
As our pure love, through early light
Shall glimmer on the dewy decks.

Sphere all your lights around, above;
Sleep, gentle heavens, before the prow;
Sleep, gentle winds, as he sleeps now,
My friend, the brother of my love;

My Arthur, whom I shall not see
Till all my widowed race be run;
Dear as the mother to the son,
More than my brothers are to me.

Alfred, Lord Tennyson (1800–92)

A Woman Waits For Me

~

A woman waits for me, she contains all,
    nothing is lacking,
Yet all were lacking if sex were lacking, or if
    the moisture
of the right man were lacking.

Through you I drain the pent-up rivers of
    myself,
In you I wrap a thousand onward years,
On you I graft the grafts of the best-beloved
    of me and America,
The drops I distil upon you shall grow fierce
    and athletic
girls, new artists, musicians, and singers,
The babes I beget upon you are to beget
    babes in their turn,
I shall demand perfect men and women out
    of my love-spendings,
I shall expect them to interpenetrate with
    others, as I and you
interpenetrate now,
I shall count on the fruits of the gushing
    showers of them,
as I count on the fruits of the gushing
    showers I give now,
I shall look for loving crops from the birth,
    life, death,
immortality, I plant so lovingly now.

Walt Whitman (1810–1892)

from *Love and Sleep*

~

And all her face was honey to my mouth,
And all her body pasture to mine eyes;
The long lithe arms and hotter hands than
    fire,
The quivering flanks, hair smelling of the
    south,
The bright light feet, the splendid supple
    thighs
And glittering eyelids of my soul's desire.
   Algernon Charles Swinburne (1837–1909)

from *Days of Wine and Roses \ Vitae Summa Brevis*

~

They are not long, the days of wine and
    roses . . .
They are not long, the weeping and the
    laughter,

Love and desire and hate.
I think they have no portion in us after
We pass the gate.

Ernest Dowson (1867–1900)

EROTICA OF THE EAST

The Eastern civilizations, with their belief in the spiritual as well as physical aspects of sex and the principle that it is the life force that motivates mankind, produced an abundance of magnificently erotic literature. Now that these cultures have to some degree embraced Western ideals, so have they embraced the sexual inhibitions of the West and the Christian principle that sex is for procreation alone, which has led to a rejection of their erotic literary history.

In Chinese erotica, symbolism is elementary: the wind and rain stand for sexual intercourse, as does "drinking at the fountain of jade". The "flute of jade" describes the male member whilst female genitalia are described variously as a peach, clouds and a lemon to name but a few. These metaphors make for truly poetic erotic writing. An example is this poem by the concubine Pan Chieh-Yu, a favorite of Emperor Ch'eng of the Han dynasty, who reigned c. 32 BC.

A Song of Grief

I took a piece of the fine cloth of Ch'i,
White silk glowing and pure like frosted
    snow,
And made you a doubled fan of union and
    joy,
As flawlessly round as the bright moon.
It comes and goes in my Lord's sleeves.
You can wave it and start a cooling breeze.
But I am always afraid that when Autumn
    comes,
And the cold blasts drive away the heat,
You will store it away in a bamboo case,
And your love of it will stop midway.

Pan Chieh-Yu
Translated by Kenneth Rexroth
and Ling Chung

THE KAMA SUTRA OF VATSYAYANA

~

The Kama Sutra (literally "the science of love") was written between the 1st and 4th centuries AD. It is an extraordinary study of sexual procedure and erotic methodology, its main tenets being that the key to maintaining an exhilarating sex life is to vary the positions of lovemaking, and that sexual bliss is linked to fulfillment and satisfaction in all areas of life.

The following excerpts are taken from Sir Richard Burton's translation, published in 1883.

from *The Kama Sutra of Vatsyayana*

~

*Of the various Ways of Lying Down and on
different Kinds of Congress*

On the occasion of a "high congress", the
Mrigi (Deer) woman should lie down in such a
way as to widen her yoni, while in a "low
congress", the Hastini (Elephant) woman
should lie down so as to contract hers. In a
"low congress" the woman should particularly
make use of medicine to cause her desires to
be satisfied quickly.

The Deer woman has the following three
ways of lying down: the widely opened
position, the yawning position and the
position of the wife of Indra. When she lowers
her head and raises her middle parts, it is
called the "widely opened position". At such a
time the man should apply some unguent, so
as to make the entrance easy. When she raises
her thighs and keeps them wide apart and

engages in congress, it is called the "yawning position". When she places her thighs with her legs doubled on them upon her sides, and thus engages in congress, it is called the position of Indrani, and this is learnt only by practice. The position is also useful in the case of the "highest congress".

The "clasping position" is used in "low congress" and in the "lowest congress", together with the "pressing position", the "twining position" and the "mare's position".

When the legs of both the male and the female are stretched straight out over each other, it is called the "clasping position". It is of two kinds, the side position and the supine position, according to the way in which they lie down. In the side position the male should invariably lie on his left side, and cause the woman to lie on her right side, and this rule is to be observed in lying down with all kinds of women.

When, after congress has begun in the clasping position, the woman presses her lover with her thighs, it is called the "pressing position".

When the woman places one of her thighs across the thigh of her lover, it is called the "twining position".

When the woman forcibly holds in her yoni the lingam after it is in, it is called the "mare's position". This is learnt by practice only, and is chiefly found among the women of the Andra country.

The above are the different ways of lying down, mentioned by Babhravya; Suvarnanabha, however, gives the following in addition.

When the female raises both of her thighs straight up, it is called the "rising position".

When she raises both of her legs, and places them on her lover's shoulders, it is called the "yawning position".

When the legs are contracted, and thus held by the lover before his bosom, it is called the "pressed position".

When only one of her legs is stretched out,

it is called the "half-pressed position".

When the woman places one of her legs on her lover's shoulder, and stretches the other out, and then places the latter on his shoulder, and stretches out the other, and continues to do so alternately, it is called the "splitting of a bamboo".

When one of her legs is placed on the head, and the other is stretched out, it is called the "fixing of a nail". This is learnt by practice only.

When both the legs of the women are contracted, and placed on her stomach, it is called the "crab's position".

When the thighs are raised and placed one upon the other, it is called the "packed position".

When a man, during congress, turns round, and enjoys the woman without leaving her, while she embraces him round the back all the time, it is called the "turning position", and is learnt only by practice.

Thus says Suvarnanabha, these different

ways of lying down, sitting and standing should be practised in water, because it is easy to do so therein. But Vatsyayana is of the opinion that congress in water is improper, because it is prohibited by the religious law.

When a man and a woman support themselves on each other's bodies or on a wall or pillar, and thus while standing engage in congress, it is called the "supported congress".

When a man supports himself against a wall, and the woman, sitting on his hands joined together and held underneath her, throws her arms round his neck, and putting her thighs alongside his waist, moves herself by her feet, which are touching the wall against which the man is leaning, it is called the "suspended congress".

When a woman stands on her hands and feet like a quadruped, and her lover mounts her like a bull, it is called the "congress of a cow". At this time everything that is ordinarily done on the bosom should be done on the back.

In the same way can be carried on the congress of a dog, the congress of a goat, the congress of a deer, the forcible mounting of an ass, the congress of a cat, the jump of a tiger, the pressing of an elephant, the rubbing of a boar, and the mounting of a horse. And in all these cases the characteristics of these different animals should be manifested by acting like them.

When a man enjoys two women at the same time, both of whom love him equally, it is called the "united congress".

When a man enjoys many women all together, it is called the "congress of a herd of cows".

The following kinds of congress – sporting in water, or the congress of an elephant with many female elephants which is said to take place only in the water, the congress of a collection of goats, the congress of a collection of deer – take place in imitation of these animals.

In Gramaneri many young men enjoy a

woman that may be married to one of them, either one after the other, or at the same time. Thus one of them holds her, another enjoys her, a third uses her mouth, a fourth holds her middle part, and in this way they go on enjoying her several parts alternately.

The same things can be done when several men are sitting in company with one courtesan, or when one courtesan is alone with many men. In the same way this can be done by the women of a king's harem when they accidentally get hold of a man.

The people in the southern countries have also a congress in the anus that is called the "lower congress".

About Women acting the Part of a Man and of the Work of a Man

When a woman sees that her lover is fatigued by constant congress, without having his desire satisfied, she should, with his permission, lay him down upon his back, and give him assistance by acting his part. She may also do this to satisfy the curiosity of her lover, or her own desire for novelty.

There are two ways of doing this, the first is when during congress she turns round and gets on the top of her lover, in such a manner as to continue the congress without obstructing the pleasure of it; and the other is when she acts the man's part from the beginning. At such a time, with flowers in her hair hanging loose, and her smiles broken by hard breathings, she should press upon her lover's bosom with her own breasts, and lowering her head frequently should do in return the same actions which he used to do before, returning his blows and chaffing him, saying, "I was laid down by you, and fatigued with hard congress, I shall now therefore lay you down in return." She should then again manifest her own bashfulness, her fatigue, and her desire of stopping the congress. In this way she should do the work of a man, which we shall presently relate.

Whatever is done by a man for giving pleasure to a woman is called the work of a man, and is as follows:

While the woman is lying on his bed, and is as it were abstracted by his conversation, he should loosen the knot of her undergarments, and when she begins to dispute with him, he should overwhelm her with kisses. Then when his lingam is erect he should touch her with his hands in various places, and gently manipulate various parts of her body. If the woman is bashful, and if it is the first time that they have come together, the man should place his hands between her thighs, which she would probably keep close together, and if she is a very young girl, he should first get his hands upon her breasts, which she would probably cover with her own hands, and under her armpits and on her neck. If however she is a seasoned woman, he should do whatever is agreeable either to him or to her, and whatever is fitting for the occasion. After this he should take hold of her hair, and hold her chin in his fingers for the purpose of kissing her. On this, if she is a young girl, she will become bashful and close her eyes. Anyhow he should gather from the action of the woman what things would be pleasing to her during congress.

Here Suvarnanabha says that while a man is doing to the woman what he likes best during congress, he should always make a point of pressing those parts of her body on which she turns her eyes.

The signs of the enjoyment and satisfaction of the woman are as follows: her body relaxes, she closes her eyes, she puts aside all bashfulness and shows increased willingness to unite the two organs as closely together as possible. On the other hand, the signs of her want of enjoyment and of failing to be satisfied are as follows: she shakes her hands, she does not let the man get up, feels dejected, bites the man, kicks him and continues to go on moving after the man has finished. In such cases the man should rub the yoni of the woman with his hand and fingers (as the elephant rubs anything with his trunk) before engaging in congress, until it is softened, and after that is done he should proceed to put his lingam into her.

The acts to be done by the man are:

> Moving forward
> Friction or churning
> Piercing
> Rubbing
> Pressing
> Giving a blow
> The blow of a boar
> The blow of a bull
> The sporting of a sparrow

When the organs are brought together properly and directly it is called "moving the organ forward".

When the lingam is held with the hand, and turned all round in the yoni, it is called "churning".

When the yoni is lowered, and the upper

part of it is struck with the lingam, it is called "piercing".

When the yoni is pressed by the lingam for a long time, it is called "pressing".

When the lingam is removed to some distance from the yoni, and then forcibly strikes it, it is called "giving a blow".

When only one part of the yoni is rubbed with the lingam, it is called the "blow of a boar".

When both sides of the yoni are rubbed in this way, it is called the "blow of a bull".

When the lingam is in the yoni, and is moved up and down frequently and without being taken out, it is called the "sporting of a sparrow". This takes place at the end of congress.

When a woman acts the part of a man, she has the following things to do in addition to the nine given above:

> The pair of tongs
> The top
> The swing

When the woman holds the lingam in her yoni, draws it in, presses it, and keeps it thus in her for a long time, it is called the "pair of tongs".

When while engaged in congress, she turns round like a wheel, it is called the "top". This is learnt by practice only.

When, on such an occasion, the man lifts up the middle part of his body and the woman turns round her middle part, it is called the "swing".

When the woman is tired, she should place her forehead on that of her lover, and should thus take rest without disturbing the union of the organs, and when the woman has rested herself the man should turn round and begin the congress again.

There are also some verses on the subject as follows:

Though a woman is reserved, and keeps her feelings concealed, yet when she gets on the top of a man, she then shows all her love and desire. A man should gather from the actions of the woman of what disposition she is, and in what way she likes to be enjoyed. A woman during her monthly courses, a woman who has been lately confined and a fat woman should not be made to act the part of a man.

On Biting, and the Ways of Love to be employed with regard to Women of Different Countries

All the places that can be kissed, are also places that can be bitten, except the upper lip, the interior of the mouth and the eyes.

Teeth of good quality are equal, possessed of a pleasing brightness, capable of being coloured, of proper proportions, unbroken and with sharp ends.

Defective teeth on the other hand are those that are blunt, protruding from the gums, rough, soft, large and loosely set.

The following are the different kinds of biting:

The hidden bite
The swollen bite
The point
The line of points
The coral and the jewel
The line of jewels
The broken cloud
The biting of the boar

The biting which is shown only by the excessive redness of the skin that is bitten, is called the "hidden bite".

When the skin is pressed down on both sides, it is called the "swollen bite".

When a small portion of the skin is bitten with two teeth only, it is called the "point".

When such small portions of the skin are bitten with all the teeth, it is called the "line of points".

The biting which is done by bringing together the teeth and the lips, is called the "coral and the jewel". The lip is the coral, and the teeth the jewel.

When biting is done with all the teeth, it is called the "line of jewels".

The biting which consists of unequal risings in a circle, and which comes from the space between the teeth, is called the "broken cloud". This is impressed on the breasts.

The biting which consists of many broad rows of marks near to one another, and with red intervals, is called the "biting of a boar". This is impressed on the breasts and the shoulders; and these two last modes of biting are peculiar to persons of intense passion.

The lower lip is the place on which the "hidden bite", the "swollen bite" and the "point" are made; the "swollen bite" and the "coral and the jewel" bite are done on the cheek. Kissing, pressing with the nails, and biting are the ornaments of the left cheek — when the word cheek is used, it is to be understood as meaning the left cheek.

Both the "line of points" and the "line of jewels" are to be impressed on the throat, the armpit and the joints of the thighs; but the "line of points" alone is to be impressed on the forehead and the thighs.

The marking with the nails, and the biting of the following things – an ornament of the forehead, an ear ornament, a bunch of flowers, a betel leaf or a tamala leaf – which are worn by or belong to the woman that is beloved, are signs of the desire of enjoyment.

Here end the different kinds of biting.

Of the various Ways of Striking and of the Sounds appropriate to them

Sexual intercourse can be compared to a quarrel, on account of the contrariness of love and its tendency to dispute. The place of striking with passion is the body, and on the body the special places are:

The shoulders
The head
The space between the breasts
The back

The jaghana, or middle part of the body

The sides

Striking is of four kinds:

Striking with the back of the hand

Striking with the fingers a little
contracted

Striking with the fist

Striking with the open palm of the
hand

On account of its causing pain, striking gives
rise to the hissing sound, which is of various
kinds, and to the eight kinds of crying:

The sound *hin*

The thundering sound

The cooing sound

The weeping sound

The sound *phut*

The sound *phât*

The sound *sût*

The sound *plât*

Besides these, there are also words having a

meaning, such as "mother", and those that are expressive of prohibition, sufficiency, desire of liberation, pain or praise, and to which may be added sounds like those of the dove, the cuckoo, the green pigeon, the parrot, the bee, the sparrow, the flamingo, the duck and the quail, which are all occasionally made use of.

Blows with the fist should be given on the back of the woman, while she is sitting on the lap of the man, and she should give blows in return, abusing the man as if she were angry, and making the cooing and the weeping sounds. While the woman is engaged in congress the space between the breasts should be struck with the back of the hand, slowly at first, and then proportionately to the increasing excitement, until the end.

At this time the sounds *hin* and others may be made, alternately or optionally, according to habit. When the man, making the sound *phut*, strikes the woman on the head, with the fingers of his hand a little contracted, it is called Prasritaka, which means striking with the fingers of the hand a little contracted. In this case the appropriate sounds are the cooing sound, the sound *phât*, the sound *phut* in the interior of the mouth and at the end of congress the sighing and weeping sounds. The sound *phât* is an imitation of the sound of a bamboo being split, while the sound *phut* is like the sound made by something falling into water. At all times, when kissing and suchlike things are begun, the woman should give a reply with a hissing sound.

During the excitement when the woman is not accustomed to striking, she continually utters words expressive of prohibition, sufficiency or desire of liberation, as well as the words "father" and "mother" intermingled with the sighing, weeping and thundering sounds.*

---

*Men who are well acquainted with the art of love are well aware how often one woman differs from another in her sighs and sounds during the time of congress. Some women like to be talked to in the most loving way, others in the most lustful way, others in the most abusive way, and so on. Some women enjoy themselves with closed eyes in silence, others make a great noise over it, and some almost faint away. The great art is to ascertain what gives them the greatest pleasure, and what specialities they like best.

THE CARNAL PRAYER MAT

~

Written by Li Yu (c. 1610–80), a Chinese
novelist and dramatist, *The Carnal Prayer
Mat* was published in 1634 and tells the
story of the Before Midnight Scholar, a
young and handsome student who dedicates
himself to a life of amatory pleasures. A
Chinese literary classic, it combines lust
with morality and describes in fascinating
detail the social and sexual mores of its time.

from *The Carnal Prayer Mat*

~

*The Before Midnight Scholar has recently
married Noble Scent but has found her wanting
in the "wind and moon" department. He buys a
book of erotic art which portrays and describes
different sexual positions in an effort to persuade
Noble Scent to become a little more adventurous.*

Up to this point Noble Scent had obediently studied the pictures and patiently listened to the commentary. But as he turned another page and began to show her Picture No. 6, she pushed the book away in visible agitation and stood up.

"Enough!" she cried. "What's the good of all these pictures? They are just upsetting. You look at them by yourself. I'm going to bed."

"Just a little patience, we'll run through the rest quickly. The best is still to come. Then we'll both go to bed."

"As if there weren't time enough tomorrow for looking at books. For my part, I've had quite enough."

He embraced her and closed her mouth with a kiss. And as he kissed her, he noticed something new. They had been married for a whole month. In all that time, she had held the gates of her teeth closed tight when he kissed her. His tongue had never succeeded in forcing or wriggling its way through the solid fence. Until today he had never made contact with her tongue; he hadn't so much as an idea of what it was like. But now when he pressed his lips to hers — what a wonderful surprise! — the tip of his tongue encountered the tip of her tongue. For the first time she had opened up the gate.

"My heart, my liver!" he sighed with delight. "At last! And now — why bother moving to the bed? This chair will do the trick, it will take the place of the rock by the pond, and we shall imitate the lovers in Picture No. 1. What do you say?"

Noble Scent with affected indignation:

"Impossible. It's not a fit occupation for human beings . . ."

"There you are perfectly right. It is an occupation and pastime more fit for the gods. Come, let us play at being gods." So saying, he stretched out his hand and began to fiddle with the knot of her sash. And despite her grimace of disapproval, she cooperated, letting him draw her close and permitting him to strip off her undermost covering. As he did so, he made a discovery that fanned his excitement into a bright flame. Aha, he thought, just looking at those pictures has sprinkled her little meadow with the dew of desire. He undid himself and set her down in the chair in such a way that her legs hung over his shoulders. Cautiously he guided his bellwether through the gates of her pleasure house, and then began to remove the rest of her clothes.

Why only now? you will ask. Why did he begin at the bottom? Let me explain: This Before Midnight Scholar was an experienced old hand. He said to himself that if he tried to remove her upper garments first, she would feel ashamed and intimidated, her resistance would make things unnecessarily difficult. That is why he daringly aimed his first offensive at her most sensitive spot, figuring that once she surrendered there she would easily surrender on all other fronts. Herein his strategy was that of the commander who defeats an enemy army by taking its General prisoner. And the truth is that she now quite willingly let him undress her from head to foot – no, not quite – with the exception of a single article of apparel which he himself tactfully spared: her little silk stockings.

After their three-inch long (or short) "golden lilies" have been bound up, our women customarily draw stockings over the bandages. Only then do their toes and ankles feel at ease. Otherwise their feet, like flowers without leaves, are unlovely to behold.

Now he too cast off his last coverings and flung himself into the fray with uplifted spear. Already his bellwether was in her pleasure house. Groping its way to left and right, slipping and sliding, it sought a passage to the secret chamber where the "flower heart," the privy seal, lies hidden. She helped him in his search by propping up her hands on the arms of the chair and, in tune with his movements, lithely twisting and bending her middle parts toward him. Thus they carried on for a time, exactly in accordance with Figure 2 of their textbook.

Suddenly, way down deep, she had a strange feeling of a kind that was utterly new to her; it did not hurt, no, it was more like a sensation of itching or tickling, almost unendurable and yet very very pleasant.

"Stop," she cried, bewildered by the strangeness of the thing. "That's enough for today. You are hurting me." And she tried to wrest herself free.

Thoroughly experienced in these matters, he realized that he had touched her most intimate spot, her flower-heart. Considerately acceding to her wishes, he moved away from the ticklish spot and contented himself with moving his bellwether slowly back and forth several dozen times through her pleasure house with its narrow passages and spacious halls. The intruder made himself thoroughly at home on her property, and she was overcome by an irresistible desire to punish him for his insolence. Choking would be a fair punishment she thought.

Removing her hands from the arms of the chair, she let his back slip down and dug her hands into his buttocks. This enabled her to press closer to him, an operation in which he helped by clasping her slender waist in his hands and holding her as tightly as he could. Thanks to the intimate conjunction thus achieved – they were now exactly in the position illustrated in Figure 3 – she held his stiff thick bellwether firmly enough to start slowly strangling it. While sparing no effort and answering pressure with pressure, he saw that her eyes were clouding over and the stately edifice of her hair was becoming undone.

"*Hsin-kan*, my heart, my liver," he panted. "You seem to be on the verge – but it is very uncomfortable in this chair; shall we not continue on the bed?"

This suggestion did not appeal to her. She

had the rascally intruder just where she wanted him; just a little longer, and she would choke the life out of him. At this last stage, she was quite unwilling to be cheated of her pleasure. If they were to move to the bed now, he would slip away from her. No, this was no time for interruptions! She shook her head resolutely. Then closing her eyes as though she were already half asleep, she said – this was her pretext – that she was much too tired to move.

He decided on a compromise: leaving her position unchanged, he placed his hands beneath her seat in such a way that she could not slip down, bade her throw her arms round his neck. Pressing his mouth to hers, he lifted her up carefully and thus enlaced carried her into the bedroom where they went on with the game.

Suddenly she let out a scream: "Dearest, ah! Ah! . . ."

She pressed closer and closer to him and the sounds that issued from her mouth were like the moans and groans of one dying. It was clear to him that she was on the threshold. And he too at the same time! With his last strength he pressed his nephrite proboscis into the sanctum of her flower-temple. Then for a time they lay enlaced as though in a deathlike sleep. She was first to stir; she heaved a deep sigh and said:

"Did you notice? I was dead just now."

"Of course I noticed. But we don't call it 'death.' We call it 'giving off an extract.'"

"What do you mean by 'giving off an extract'?"

"Both in man and woman a subtle essence of all the bodily humors is at all times secreted. At the peak of amorous pleasure one of the body's vessels overflows and gives off some of this extract. Just before the flow, the whole body, skin and flesh and bones, falls into a deep, unconscious sleep. Our physical state before, during, and after the flow is called *tiu* 'a giving off of extract.' It is depicted in Figure 5."

"Then I was not dead?"

"Of course not. You gave off an extract."

"If that is so, I hope I may do it day after day and night after night."

The Before Midnight Scholar is forced to realize that he is not as well-endowed as he thought. (He consequently decides to have his penis enlarged – using a piece of canine flesh – in order to achieve his amorous aspirations.)

"I want to know first of all, what I am determined to see with my own eyes is this: how big is your implement in reality, or to be precise, how many inches long is it?"

"Well, it's not exactly little. That should satisfy you."

"But it doesn't. Come, show it," the other insisted and reached unceremoniously for the young man's trousers in the intention of pulling them down. The young man resisted and struggled loose twice or three times. He was quite unwilling to lay himself bare.

"Very well then. I won't insist. But I am forced to assume that you are afraid to show your implement because it is just too insignificant. In that case, I regret to say that I can no longer act in your behalf. Just imagine, if you please, the embarrassing consequences if you should approach an exacting young lady with your inadequate article. She will not feel the slightest tickle of pleasure. In her rage and disappointment, she will make a terrible fuss! She will scream like a madwoman and accuse you of trying to rape her. The scandal you would provoke with such folly is beyond imagining. And you expect me to get mixed up in such a mess, to shoulder the responsibility for such a fiasco? No indeed, you can count me out."

Under the pressure of these convincing arguments, the young man finally gave in.

"It's not at all as you suspect," he stammered with a sheepish smile. "My implement can bear inspection. I was only embarrassed to display it in broad daylight, even to a friend. But since you insist, I shall comply, if only to dispel your unwarranted suspicions. Here you are."

He opened his fly and brought out the witness to his manhood, a device compounded of the tenderest flesh and the finest membranes. He laid it in the palm of his right hand, and as though to gauge its weight, flipped it up and down a few times before the other's eyes.

"Permit me to introduce my humble equipment, my modest implement."

The other took a step closer to examine it in detail. What did he see?

A pale, white stalk
A pointed bright-red blossom
Beneath a copse of sparse hair,
Veins and sinews barely discernible,
Length barely two inches
Weight three ounces at most –
A frail tube –
One might mistake it for the thin tube

In which a Mongol collects camel hairs.
The head with the fine slit
Might be taken for the bowl of a tobacco
*   pipe*
Such as those smoked by the women of the
*   northern steppes.*
An article suited at most
To a maiden of thirteen
A pleasure boy of fourteen
Might take some joy in it.
Before the battle it burgeons into a hard
*   stylus,*
And then it resembles a parched razor
*   clam.*
Afterward it bends like a bow
And shrivels till it looks like a dried crab.

After a thorough inspection the elder brother raised his eyes and stared at the young man in silence. "He is speechless with amazement over my impressive equipment," thought the younger brother and remarked complacently:

"You have seen nothing. This is how it looks afterward when it is weary of battle. But before the battle starts – then it is something to see. Then you would have something to stare about."

"Quite unnecessary. I am perfectly satisfied with what I have already seen. Now I know what is what. Put it away," the elder brother motioned and burst into an uproarious laugh.

"My good friend. How can anyone be so completely bereft of eyesight and judgment? Your equipment is not even a third as large as that of the average man. And with that you planned to invade strange houses and seduce other people's wives. Ha ha! Does it seem likely that a woman whose gate is as wide as a shoe and who is dissatisfied with her husband's last would attempt to fill out the gap with your pitiful stylus? The way you boast, the way you chase after women wherever you go, I really expected to see something impressive, a bludgeon to strike awe in any woman's heart. I hesitated at first to ask for evidence. How could I suspect that you had nothing more than that deplorable scratch-pen, fit perhaps to fumble round a while in your companion's moss and bushes, but quite incapable of penetrating the innermost passages of her pleasure house."

The Before Midnight Scholar has left Noble Scent in the care of her overbearing father, and is traveling the land, ostensibly to improve his chances of a high place in the State examinations. But with freedom comes temptation, and it's not long before the handsome student finds himself improving his education in other areas. His new love, Aroma, has tricked the Before Midnight Scholar into believing that he has just made love to her, when really Aroma's place has been taken by her rather plain neighbor. The neighbor leaves and, after bathing him, Aroma allows the student to take her to bed.

He moved her carefully into place, raised her

legs over his shoulders, and opened the battle, employing the same tactics as with her ugly precursor; a frontal attack without introductory love play. His calculation was that though this approach might hurt her at first, her pleasure would be all the greater afterward. The offensive ran off without a hitch. But contrary to his expectations, she remained utterly apathetic as though she felt nothing at all, giving no sign either of pleasure or of pain. Then he remembered what his experienced friend, K'un-lun's Rival, had told him about the mighty caliber of her husband's last. No wonder his forces had been able to slip into the enemy fortress so easily, without encountering the least resistance. He had not been prepared for a shoe of such dimensions. In a shoe so deep and wide his last, though by no means unimpressive, seemed to shrivel into nothingness, to lose itself like a needle in a haystack.

Aware that he would get nowhere by the

old methods, he decided on a change of tactics. Removing the pillow from under Aroma's head, he pushed it beneath her loins. In so doing, he intentionally neglected to provide her head with another support. This impressed her and inspired her with a secret admiration. Thus far she had experienced no pleasure at all, but she saw by his preparations that he knew a thing or two about bedchamber technique and was confident that everything would come out all right in the end.

Esteemed reader, the battle of the sexes is in many respects not unlike the art of warfare: before the opening of hostilities, the two contestants spy upon each other, feeling out one another's strengths and weaknesses. He tries to find out whether she is deep or not so deep, in order to plan his offensive and retreat accordingly. She tries to obtain accurate information about his armament, whether short or long, thick or thin, in order to meet it with suitable movements and adapt herself to it. Success in battle depends on knowledge of the enemy's strength or weakness. The length and thickness of men's utensils vary exceedingly, and the same applies to the depth and width of women's pleasure houses. If she is not particularly deep, an over-long utensil is out of place; there will not be room for it, at least not for all of it. If he should nevertheless attempt to force the whole of it in, he will give her not pleasure but pain. Ought he to get all the pleasure? That would be unfair. But if she possesses an extraordinarily deep pleasure grotto, she needs a mate with unusually long and powerful armament; otherwise she will get no satisfaction. But the length of the male organ is fixed by nature once and for all; it does not go on growing and there is no way of lengthening it artificially.

Consequently a knowing lover resorts to a stratagem: he removes the pillow from beneath his lady's head and wedges it under her waist. Thus raised, her pelvis lies flatter and the lover's utensil is so enabled to reach the bottom. This should not be taken to mean that the pillow beneath the waist is indispensable or should be employed in every case. It is indicated only in cases when the lady's pleasure grotto is too deep for her lover's armament. We see then that this shortcoming can be remedied. But there is another discrepancy that cannot be made good: when the lady's shoe is too wide for her lover's last.

The itinerant surgeon's operation had considerably increased the thickness and stamina of our young man's equipment, but had not lengthened it. On his first attempt to penetrate Aroma's pleasure grotto, his utensil had proved too short and had failed to plumb the depths. By hitting on the above-mentioned stratagem of wedging the pillow under her waist, he had impressed her with his competence; she said nothing but secretly she was very pleased.

This use of a pillow is a simple and widely known trick, but few men are considerate enough to bother and still fewer know how to do the thing properly. In addition to supporting the waist, most men leave the pillow under their lady's head. This is a big mistake. For her body is then raised at both ends, with the result that she is bent in the middle. If, to make matters worse, her lover rests his whole weight upon her, it is easy to imagine how uncomfortable she must feel. In this unnatural position, a kiss requires the most painful contortions on both sides: he must hump his back in order to reach her mouth; she must stretch her neck and twist her head backward before her lips and tongue can meet his lips and tongue. All this because of the troublesome and superfluous pillow under her head. And so I say, away with it! Let the lady's cloud-coiffure lie directly on the sheet. Then the heads and limbs of both parties will fit harmoniously together; his noble yak whisk will penetrate her pleasure grotto without difficulty, her purple little tongue will find its way easily into his mouth, no inequalities of position will prevent them from merging and blending inwardly, no discomfort will mar their pleasure.

After this brief digression, let us get on with our story. Raising her nephrite thighs over his shoulders, planting both hands on the bed sheet, our scholar resumed the interrupted battle – this time with success. His valiant henchman did not bely his partly canine origins and nature. The longer the battle raged, the more imposing became his stature and with it his courage; no longer was her pleasure grotto a bottomless pit; both on the sides and in the depths the desired contact was established. Aroma's attitude changed accordingly. The first assault had left her totally apathetic and inert, no sound of pleasure or pain had escaped her, but now her body began to quiver and writhe voluptuously, and moans of *"hach . . . hh . . ."* issued from her lips.

"*Hsin-kan*, dearest. It's coming! I feel a pleasant sensation."

"So soon? Why, I've hardly begun," he whispered back. "Just wait until I get going, then you will really feel something, *wo-ti kuai jou*, my perverse little lump of flesh." And he proceeded to heave and thrash until heaven and earth were stricken with terror and threatened to lose their balance. Her stifled cries of "Dearest" and "Oh, I'm dying" became more and more frequent and the grass and bushes round her gate grew moist with the dew of pleasure. He reached for the sweat cloth to wipe away the dew, but she restrained him. How so? It has already been stated that she was very passionate by nature. A battle of the sexes, she felt, should be a wild frenzy, an ecstatic temple dance with a rousing accompaniment of gongs and drums. Interrupt the temple dance with a prosaic sweat cloth? Out of the question. Even in her everyday dealings with her husband she had taken the same attitude. Let the dew of pleasure sprinkle her as it might, there would be no wiping until afterward, after the cloud had burst. This was a very personal eccentricity of hers. I mention it only in passing and – it goes without saying – only for the benefit of gourmets and connoisseurs!

Our young man was still going strong when she flung her arms round his neck, pressed him close, and groaned: "*Wo yao tiu la!* My cloud is bursting. Let us die of joy together."

Actually it was too soon for him. He would have been glad to go on a little longer and impress her with his vigor and endurance. But she would not allow it.

"Stop. I am fully convinced of your strength and endurance. You've been battling all through the night, you've taken on two women and laid them low. Grant yourself a little rest, save your strength for tomorrow night; I shouldn't like you to get sick from overexertion; I want you to stay well for my sake."

Ah, she was concerned for his health. How considerate! How touching! Deeply moved, he folded her in his arms, pressed her tight, and body to body, they shared the ineffable bliss of the bursting cloud.

THE PERFUMED GARDEN

~

Written in the 16th century by the Tunisian
Shaykh Umar ibn Muhammed al-Nefzawi,
this most famous of Arab love manuals was
translated by Richard Burton, explorer and
orientalist, and published in 1886. A classic
of unadulterated, guilt-free eroticism, it is
rated alongside its Sanskrit counterpart, *The
Kama Sutra*.

from *The Perfumed Garden*

~

The kiss on the mouth, on the two cheeks,
upon the neck, as well as the sucking up of
fresh lips, are gifts of God, destined to
provoke erection at the favourable moment.
God also is it who has embellished the chest
of the woman with breasts, has furnished her
with a double chin, and has given brilliant
colours to her cheeks.

He has also gifted her with eyes that inspire love, and with eyelashes like polished blades.

He has furnished her with a rounded belly and a beautiful navel, and with a majestic crupper; and all these wonders are borne up by the thighs. It is between these latter that God has placed the arena of the combat; when the same is provided with ample flesh, it resembles the head of a lion. It is called the vulva. Oh! How many men's deaths lie at her door? Amongst them how many heroes!

∾

When both man and woman are fat, and wish to unite in coition, they cannot contrive to do it without trouble, particularly when both have prominent stomachs. In these circumstances the best way to go about it is for the woman to be on her knees with her hands on the ground, so that her posterior is elevated; then the man separates her legs, leaving the points of the feet close together and the heels parted asunder; he then attacks her from behind, kneeling and holding up his stomach with his hand, and so introduces his member. Resting his stomach upon her buttocks during the act, he holds the thighs or the waist of the woman with his hands. If her posterior is too low for his stomach to rest upon, he must place a cushion under her knees to remedy this.

I know of no other position so favourable as this for the coition of a fat man with a fat woman.

~

If you desire coition, place the woman on the ground, cling closely to her bosom, with her lips close to yours; then clasp her to you, suck her breath, bite her; kiss her breasts, her stomach, her flanks, press her close in your arms, so as to make her faint with pleasure; when you see her so far gone, then push your member into her. If you have done as I said, the enjoyment will come to both of you simultaneously. This it is which makes the pleasure of the woman so sweet. But if you neglect my advice the woman will not be satisfied, and you will not have procured her any pleasure.

The coition being finished, do not get up at once, but come down softly on her right side, and if she has conceived, she will bear a male child, if it please God on high!

HOMOEROTICA

The Greeks regarded the sexual congress between a man and a youth as acceptable, as far as the active male homosexual role was concerned, but the youth, in allowing himself to be passive, was seen to have cast himself into the lower category of women and slaves.

The Romans were much influenced by the phallus worship of the Greeks and it became a constant source of material for Latin erotic literature, producing writing and poetry more lighthearted and bawdy than that of ancient Greece.

In the periods covered by this book, most of the erotic writers were men, so unfortunately girls lose out (except for Sappho) in these extracts from predominantly male homosexual literature.

. . . for as I look briefly at you, so can I no longer speak at all, my tongue is silent, broken, a silken fire suddenly has spread beneath my skin, with my eyes I see nothing, my hearing hums, a cold sweat grips me, a trembling seizes me entire, more pale than grass am I, I seem to myself to be little short of dead.

Sappho (7th century BC)

It was you, Atthis, who said

"Sappho, if you will not get
up and let us look at you
I shall never love you again!

"Get up, unleash your suppleness,
lift off your Chian nightdress
and, like a lily leaning into

"a spring, bathe in the water.
Cleis is bringing your best
purple frock and the yellow

"tunic from the clothes chest;
you will have a cloak thrown over
you and flowers crowning your hair . . .

"Praxinoa, my child, will you please
roast nuts for our breakfast? One
of the gods is being good to us:

"today we are going at last
into Mitylene, our favorite
city, with Sappho, loveliest

"of its women; she will walk
among us like a mother with

all her daughters around her

"when she comes home from exile . . ."

But you forget everything

Sappho (7th century BC)
Translated by Mary Barnard

I entrust all to you, Aurelius,
And I ask this modest favour in return:
If ever you have wished to keep something
    pure
Then guard this darling of my heart from
    danger.
I don't mean protect him from the common
    herd
Who wander through the streets involved in
    themselves,
But save him rather from your own great
    penis
Which is lethal to any boy, good or bad.
You can display yourself wherever you please
And indulge your lust whenever you want to.

I only ask this modest request: spare *him*.
But if you commit that most heinous of
   crimes,
Then I pity the lust that drives you to it,
For I'll fetter your feet and shove through
   the gate
Of your arse radishes and the fins of mullet,
Punishing you like a common adulterer.

Catullus (c. 84–c. 54 BC)

from *Odes*, 1,4

❧

Far from the tender Tribe of Boys remove,
For they've a thousand ways to kindle Love.
This, pleases as he strides the manag'd
   Horse,
And holds the taughten'd Rein with early
   Force;
This, as he swims, delights the Fancy best,
Raising the smiling Wave with snowy Breast:
This, with a comely Look and manly Airs;

And that with Virgin Modesty ensnares.
But if at first you find him not inclin'd
To Love, have Patience, Time will change his
   Mind.

Tibullus (c. 60–19 BC)

To Phoebus

~

Lying with unstable pego 'twixt a brace of
   vigorous boys,
Phoebus what's the little game that all your
   leisure time employs?
I should guess, but contradicting rumours
   from your friends odd rot 'em,
Check the surmise that you open to these
   vigorous youths your bottom;
Rumour with its hundred tongues, that tells
   us you're not up to fucking,
Tells us that you are not buggered; what's
   then left for you but sucking?

Martial (c. AD 40–104)

A Riddle

Young Hyllus, why refuse today
What yesterday you freely granted,
Suddenly harsh and obdurate,
Who once agreed to all I wanted.

You plead your beard, your weight of years,
Your hairy chest in mitigation?
To turn a boy into a man
How long then was the night's duration?

Why, Hyllus, do you mock at me,
Turning affection into scorning?
If last night you were still a boy,
How can you be a man this morning?

Martial (c. AD 40–104)
Translated by Brian Hill

from *Satire Nine*

~

*Naevolus' reply to Juvenal's comment that he
looks like a man changed for the worse.*

NAEVOLUS:

Many men have done well from my way of
    life,

But I've got precious little out of it.
    Sometimes I've been given

An old, greasy cloak to cover my toga –

Some coarsely woven, coarsely dyed rag
    made by a peasant in France –

And sometimes I get a hand-me-down
    geegaw made out of low grade silver.

But Destiny's our master! Fate even rules
    what's under our clothes,

And if the stars are against you the fantastic
    size of your cock gets you nowhere.

Even if Virro did slobber when he saw your
    naked charms

And sent love letters by the hundred, lewdly

misquoting Homer for fun:
"A man is attracted by the very sight of – a
    pansy or queen."
There is nothing worse than a tight-fisted,
    debauched old queer.
"I gave you *this* much," he says, "and then I
    gave you *that* amount afterwards,
And then I gave you ever so much more."
    Lust at piece-rate!
"Well," I said, "let's do the thing properly and
    call in an accountant.
Cough up five thousand miserly sesterces
    and *I'll* say what *I've* earned.
I suppose you think it's fun, stuffing my
    prick up so far
That it hits your dinner. *Real* ploughboys
    earn far more!"
"You used to call yourself handsome," he
    said, "and the Ganymede *de nos jours.*"
"But when will a man like you (you won't
    even pay for his pleasures)
Show kindness to a poor follower? *And* you
    want presents," I added.

"Who expects green sunshades and amber
beads when his birthday comes round
And lolls on his day-bed, counting his gifts
at Ladies' Day?
What are all those hill farms at Apulia for,
you lecherous sparrow,
And all those acres of meadow that would
tire a kite to cross?
Your stores are filled with plump grapes from
your vineyard slopes
At Cumae, Gaurus and Trifoli – enough for
a lifetime's drinking!
Would it be too much to give a few acres to
these exhausted loins?
Do you really think it's better to give a
countrywoman, her cottage, her baby and
her dog
To some cymbal-clashing boyfriend? "How
rude you are!" you scream.
"Yes, but I've got to pay my rent and my
single slaveboy.
(That's right. Just the one. I need another,
and that's two to feed.)

I suppose I'm expected to pray when winter
    howls around!
But what about their frozen bodies when
    December's north wind blows?
Shall I tell the lads: "OK, hang on, wait till
    summer and the cicadas come?"
If you ignore my other services, how do you
    price this one:
Were I not your faithful servant, your wife
    would still be a virgin?
How often have you asked that of me and
    what promises you made!
She'd be near to doing a bunk when I bedded
    her for you
And would have torn up the marriage
    licence if it hadn't been for my hard work.
When you were crying outside the door. The
    bed – and you
Who heard the groaning inside – are
    witnesses to these facts.
There's many a household been saved by
    timely adultery, you know.
So what are you going to do? Which was the

best of my services?
Is it nothing to a bastard like you that I have
given you a son and a daughter?
No – *you* rear the children and publish your
virility in the papers,
Hang garlands at your door! You're a father!
No one can spread rumours.
And you have paternal rights and all that tax
relief through me!
Your children make you heir to a fortune,
and there's more if I get you a third."

JUVENAL:

You've reason to complain, Naevolus, but
what does he say?

NAEVOLUS:

He takes no notice and looks for another
two-legged donkey,
Another just like me. But this must stay a
secret, please.
These pumice-smoothed queens make the
worst enemies – and he suspects.
He'd stop at nothing: the sword, a clubbing

or burning my house.

And just you remember that poison is cheap
   for a wealthy man.

So don't split on me. This matter is highly
   confidential.

Juvenal (AD 59–130)

from *Satire Two*

~

You'll sacrifice the stomach of a pig and a
   vast bowl of wine while ensuring

That only males come in. "Clear out!
   Women are profane!

No music from she-minstrels here!" Such
   were the cries and the rites

In Athens . . . One queen is using an eyebrow
   pencil,

A needle stained with damp soot. She puts
   on mascara.

Another drinks from a phallic cup and ties
   her hair

In a glittering net. Her cheeks are blue or
smooth and green.

Juvenal (AD 59–130)

Epigrams from *The Greek Anthology* (c. 429 BC–AD 600)

~

Hetero-sex is best for the man of a serious
turn of mind,
But here's a hint, if you should fancy the
other:
Turn Menophila round in bed, address her
peachy behind.
And it's easy to pretend you're screwing her
brother.

Marcus Argentarius
Translated by Fleur Adcock

Nicander, ooh, your leg's got hairs!
Watch they don't creep up into your arse.

Because, darling, if they do, you'll soon know
How the lovers flee you, and years go.

Alkaios
Translated by Tony Harrison

from *Ganymede and Helen*

~

I saw where Ganymede with Helen went
On summer grass beneath a lovely pine:
Serene their faces' so majestic line
That shamed the rose and lily in them blent.

Then seemed they both to sit upon the
    ground
Which to their lovely looks did often smile.
Such beauty gods alone have to beguile,
Yet both did wonder at the grace they found.

There they discussed a host of things, I ween,
And then about their beauties did debate;
They seemed two gods competing in their
    state,

The boy comparing him unto the queen.

She, longing for a man and fit for bed,
Could feel the goading pangs of cruel sex;
The comeliness of Ganymede did vex
And inner fires did glow an outward red.

Though Shame will turn her from love's
    place of rest,
The woman had no more a virgin's ice,
And, since she was not asked, she dared
    entice,
Off'ring the boy her lap, her mouth, her
    breast.

Though both were stretched upon the grass
    so free
And union been blessed between the two,
Young Ganymede, not knowing what to do,
Pressed close to her that he might passive be.

She senses something's wrong and in amaze
She pushes him aside, she weeps, she rails,
She curses nature and the gods bewails
That so unnatural had so fair a gaze.

The argument develops to a fight:
She praises womankind, the male he,
Till Nature and Reason are called to be
The judges and determiners of right.

HELEN:

"Alas," says Helen, "much my pity runs
Since womankind cold-heartedly you spurn
And so the natural order overturn
Why had you father if you'll have no sons?"

GANYMEDE:

"Sons from old men will please a young
    man's zest
For he has lust to pleasure youthful May.
The gods' invention is the game we play
Which still is followed by the bright and
    best."

HELEN:

"But merely ornamental is your face
And hastes to perish since you have no wife.
If you should marry and beget new life

A son's fresh form his father's would
    replace."

GANYMEDE:
"I have no wish my features to repair;
I pleasure men with me uniquely made.
I hope with time your beauties all will fade
For I am less beloved since you are fair."

HELEN:
"How lovely are the different sexes' loves
When men and women mutually entwine;
By natural attraction they combine
As do the beasts, the boars and e'en the
    doves."

GANYMEDE:
"But mankind should not rut like pigs and
    birds
For humans have the power of thought
    divine,
And only peasants – those we may call
    swine –
Are born as men to loose to female herds."

HELEN:

"No love has ever touched a boyish heart,
That's man and woman's coupled in one bed;
For proper union's achieved, it's said,
When both the sexes are distinct, apart."

GANYMEDE:

"But things are sundered by disparity;
More elegant are men joined each to each.
Perhaps you're ignorant of rules of speech:
The adjective and noun must both agree."

HELEN:

"When first the great Creator formed the
    male
He tried to make the woman yet more fair
So drawn to her the man might have an heir
And men's regard for men would not
    prevail."

GANYMEDE:

"The love of women I might have agreed
Was good if manners went with looks by
    right,
But married women sully love's delight,

While those unmarried serve the public
    need."

HELEN:
"Then let men blush and Nature grieve as
    well;
That men should join was never yet her
    mind.
Men yoked by Venus fruitless coupling find.
This boy, despite his sex, his charms will
    sell."

GANYMEDE:
"Such worthy love each worthy man employs,
The highly placed such passion highly rate,
And men who moral matters arbitrate
Are not averse to loving soft-thighed boys."

HELEN:
"I don't count those whom frenzied lusts
    deprave,
No reason can for your defence conspire.
This youngster here has never felt desire
And so his wickedness is yet more grave."

GANYMEDE:

"The smell of profit is a pleasing one
Whose sure appeal many men acclaim;
To gather riches most go on the game,
For men who want a boy will pay for fun."

HELEN:

"Even if this were not a sin for youth,
For older men there's simply no excuse;
I have to laugh at their absurd abuse.
It is a sin in dotage, that's the truth."

GANYMEDE:

"Your accusations of the old are just.
It seems disgraceful when their hairs are grey
To join the pleasures of the young and gay.
But they should not discourage boyish lust."

HELEN:

"But tell me, lad, when youthful good looks
    fade,
With wrinkled face and beard that's more
    than fluff,
With chest turned bushy and your arsehole
    tough,

Will you be still the prize whence dreams are
    made?"

GANYMEDE:

"When by the years your virgin charms are
    marred,
Your lips have thickened and your skin is dry,
When crowfoot's drooping round your misty
    eye,
Won't your most ardent lover be half-hard?"

HELEN:

"You try to keep as hairless as a sylph
And imitate a woman with your ass;
Defying nature you become a lass
And war on her with such unnatural filth."

GANYMEDE:

"I'd like to be both soft and smooth, 'tis true,
But God forbid I had a woman's fane.
My softness puts off girls whom I disdain.
What difference between a mule and you?"

HELEN:

"Oh, were I not restrained by modesty
I'd not be mincing words with you, my son;

But I'll not be heard swearing, it's not done,
For foul words are a slight to modesty."

GANYMEDE:

"But we came here to speak of vulgar acts,
This is no place to show the modest mind,
For piety and shame were left behind
And I shan't spare your maiden's airs nor
        facts."

HELEN:

"I don't know where to turn, for I must prate
With equal viciousness or loser be,
But if I strive for an equality
My virtue with a prostitute's will rate."

GANYMEDE:

"Go try your lies on someone more naive!
Flat on your back you've propositioned men.
Where was such a dove-like innocence then?
This sudden change am I meant to believe?"

HELEN:

"But when a man a boy in congress meets
(The sort of man who rashly gelds his males)

The horrid sin o'er both of them prevails
And, shame to say, the morning shows
    stained sheets."

GANYMEDE:

"The man into whose bed a strumpet slinks
And whose delight is filthy woman's quim,
When tarts recumbent open up to him
Learns all too well how their bilge water
    stinks."

HELEN:

"Tarts smell like tarts and they are bound to
    cloy,
But girls excel the balsam's fragrant bliss;
There's honey on their lips and in their kiss,
And blest the man who virgins can enjoy."

GANYMEDE:

"When Jupiter divides him in his bed
And turns to Juno first then to his boy
He swiftly leaves his wife for proper joy,
Returns to quarrel, then takes me instead."

HELEN:

"Your wretched Venus' fruitless, sterile art
Causes the love of women to decay;
When man mounts man in this disgraceful
    way
And monstrous Venus fakes the woman's
    part."

GANYMEDE:

"It is not monstrous monsters to avoid:
The sticky bush, the darkly yawning cave,
The hole whose stink all others will
    outbrave;
Nor pole nor oar will e'er come near that
    void."

HELEN:

"Be quiet, be quiet, such words are a disgrace!
Just talk more decently, you filthy pup!
If for a modest girl you won't shut up,
At least to Nature and the gods give place."

GANYMEDE:

"If such things in cloaks of words you'd cover,
By such a tricked out truth you may beguile,

But I'll not help in gilding what is vile:
Words and actions both must suit each
    other."

HELEN:
"Then I'll put by the cloak of shame and fear
Since now I am obliged to speak so plain:
When impure coupling you entertain
Between your thighs you lose the precious
    tear.
There's the unutterable disgrace:
My words are nasty but your deeds are base."
The youth hears the unmentionable crime,
A stupor stops his speech and blushes rise
And furtive tears steal warmly from his eyes.
Lacking defence, he does not speak this
    time.
Now in his silence Reason from her throne
Speaks prudently with fitting words though
    few:
"Here needs no judge, the matter's plain to
    view.
I say 'Enough. The boy is overthrown.'"
                              Anon (12th century)

Epitaph for Jean Maillard

Jean Maillard lies buried here,
Less a wide-boy than a queer
Who believed that if desire
Set a tutor's flesh on fire
Then a true-born Sorbonite
Could become a sodomite
Without any fear of vice
Because the action was so nice.
But, afraid that woman's lip
Just might let his secret slip
And so scandalize the rest,
Our good master thought it best
In case he was discovered
To ensure he was covered
By this fair expedient:
She could borrow him for rent.

Anon (c. 1570)

To Corydon

This Quintus, Corydon, for whom you lust,
Dry, hollow-boned boy as saffron yellow,
He has no blood, his veins are filled with dust,
There is no sweating passion to the fellow!
An Ethiope usurped his father's place
Engendering some dusky offspring there.
Provoke his smile and you'll get a grimace
As if you'd shown the cunt of some old mare.
So smell his mouth. "It is an arse," you'll say,
But sure an arse is cleaner than that gob.
Your dick will shrink for ever and a day
If once you try to kiss the putrid slob.
So, clear off, Quintus, you clapped, poxy whore,
   whore,
Go where you please, you poisoner of cocks,
As many men are lost in your great maw
As ships are wrecked on the Sicilian rocks.
Yet publicly he does what women do,
This common tart gives every man the
   goods,

And he who such a boy would wish to screw
Would let the wild beasts shag him in the
    woods!

'Panormitanus' (15th century)
Translated by Antonio Beccadelli

Brother Astolfo sated appetite
By rubbing off against a choirboy's bum
Until the ground was all a-wash with cum.
Was he, therefore, a sinful sodomite?
No, he was not. Brother Astolfo went
Not in the bum but on the surface skin
And since such friction is not deemed a sin
It constitutes no cause for punishment.

Pietro Aretino (1492–1556)

Song

Love a woman? You're an ass!
'Tis a most insipid passion
To choose out for your happiness
The silliest part of God's creation.

Let the porter and the groom,
Things designed for dirty slaves,
Drudge in fair Aurelia's womb
To get supplies for age and graves.

Farewell, woman! I intend
Henceforth every night to sit
With my lewd, well natured friend,
Drinking to engender wit.

Then give me health, wealth, mirth, and
    wine
And, if busy love entrenches,
There's a sweet, soft page of mine
Does the trick worth forty wenches.

John Wilmot, Earl of Rochester (1648–80)

from *West-Easterly Divan, Book 9*

~

The Cupbearer Speaks

Prithee leave me, crafty hussy,
Take thy ringlets brown away:
To my master suits my waiting
And his kisses are my pay.

Therefore thou, I'm free to wager,
Has no love on me to spend:
And thy cheeks, thy breasts, would only
Be fatiguing to my friend.

Dost thou really think to trick me
Thus to leave as if so shy?
I will lie upon the threshold,
Watching lest thou slippest by.

Johann Wolfgang von Goethe (1749–1832)
Translated by John Weiss

We Two Boys Together Clinging
~

We two boys together clinging,
One the other never leaving
Up and down the roads going,
North and South excursions making,
Power enjoying, elbows stretching, fingers
    clutching,
Arm'd and fearless, eating, drinking,
    sleeping, loving,
No law less than ourselves owning, sailing,
    soldiering, thieving, threatening,
Misers, menials, priests alarming, air
    breathing, water drinking, on the turf or
    the sea-beach dancing,
Cities wrenching, ease scorning, statutes
    mocking, feebleness chasing,
Fulfilling our foray.

Walt Whitman (1819–92)

A Bad Sleeper

He is a bad sleeper and it is a joy to me
To feel him well when he is the proud prey
And the strong neighbour of the best of
     sleep
Without false covers – no need – and
     without awakenings.
So near, so near to me that I believe he
     enflames me
In some way, with his overwhelming desire,
     that I feel
In my ravished and trembling body.
If we find ourselves face to face, and if he
     turns
Close to my side, as lovers are wont to do,
His haunches, deliriously dreamy or not,
Sudden, mutinous, malicious, stubborn,
     whorish,
In the name-of-God, his cravings, so gentle,
     will pierce my flesh,
And leave me girdled like a eunuch,

Or if I should turn to him with the wish
To soothe him; or, if peacefully we lie, his
    quietness,
Brutal and gentle, will suffuse my body in his;
And my spirit, out of happiness, will
    submerge and overwhelm him,
And prostrate him, infinite in that tack.
Am I happy? Totus in benigno positus!

Paul Verlaine (1844–1896)
Translated by Francois Pirou

from *Chansons de Bilitis*

～

The Complaisant Friend

The storm lasted all night. Selenis, with her
lovely hair, came to spin with me. She stayed
for fear of the mud, and we filled my little
bed, clasped close to each other. When two
girls go to bed together, sleep stays at the
door. "Bilitis, tell me, whom do you love?" To

caress me softly she slipped her leg over mine. And over my mouth she said: "Bilitis, I know whom you love. Shut your eyes. I am Lycas!" I answered, touching her: "Can I not see that you are a girl? Your pleasantry is out of place." But she rejoined: "I am really Lycas, if you shut your lids. Here are his arms, and here are his hands . . ." And in the silence she tenderly delighted my dreaming with a singular vision.

Pierre Louys (1870–1925)

TELENY *or* THE REVERSE
OF THE MEDAL

~

The first edition of *Teleny*, or *The Reverse of the Medal*, was published in 1883 and limited to 200 copies. Written by an anonymous writer but often attributed to Oscar Wilde, it tells the story of Monsieur Camille Des Grieux's obsession with René Teleny, a pianist. Narrated by Des Grieux, the following describes his first meeting with Teleny.

from *Teleny*

~

The pianist stretched forth his ungloved hand. In my fit of nervousness I had pulled off both my gloves, so that I now put my bare hand into his. He had a perfect hand for a man, rather large than small, strong yet soft, and with long, tapering fingers, so that his grasp was firm and steady.

Who has not been sentient of the manifold feelings produced by the touch of a hand? Many persons seem to bear a temperature of their own about them. They are hot and feverish in mid-winter, while others are cold and icy in the dog-days. Some hands are dry and parched, others continually moist, clammy, and slimy. There are fleshy, pulpy, muscular, or thin, skeleton and bony hands. The grasp of some is like that of an iron vice, others feel as limp as a bit of rag. There is the artificial product of our modern civilisation, a deformity like a Chinese lady's foot, always enclosed in a glove during the day, often poulticed at night, tended by a manicure; they are as white as snow, if not as chaste as ice. How that little useless hand would shrink from the touch of the gaunt, horny, clay-coloured, begrimed workman's hand, which hard, unremitting labour has changed into a kind of hoof. Some hands are coy, others paddle you indecently; the grip of some is hypocritical, and not what it pretends to be; there is the velvety, the unctuous, the priestly, the humbug's hand; the open palm of the spendthrift, the usurer's tight-fisted claw. There is, moreover, the magnetic hand, which seems to have a secret affinity for your own; its simple touch thrills your whole nervous system, and fills you with delight.

How can I express all that I felt from the contact of Teleny's hand? It set me on fire; and, strange to say, it soothed me at the same time. How sweeter, softer, it was, than any woman's kiss. I felt his grasp steal slowly over all my body, caressing my lips, my throat, my breast; my nerves quivered from head to foot with delight, then it sank downwards into my reins, and Priapus, re-awakened, uplifted his head. I actually felt I was being taken possession of, and I was happy to belong to him.

And later, after a performance by Teleny,

watched by Des Grieux:

"Did you not see me turn round during the gavotte, and look for you? I began to feel you just then, but I could not find you out; you remember, don't you?"

"Yes, I did see you look towards my side, and – "

"And you were jealous!"

"Yes," said I, almost inaudibly.

He pressed my arms strongly against his body for all answer, then after a pause, he added hurriedly, and in a whisper:

"You must know that I do not care for a single girl in this world, I never did, I could never love a woman."

My heart was beating strongly; I felt a choking feeling as if something was gripping my throat.

Why should he be telling me this? said I to myself.

"Did you not smell a scent just then?"

"A scent – when?"

"When I was playing the gavotte; you have forgotten perhaps."

"Let me see, you are right, what scent was it?"

"Lavande ambrée."

"Exactly."

"Which you do not care for, and which I dislike; tell me, which is your favourite scent?"

"Heliotrop blanc."

Without giving me an answer, he pulled out his handkerchief and gave it to me to smell.

"All our tastes are exactly the same, are they not?" And saying this, he looked at me with such a passionate and voluptuous longing, that the carnal hunger depicted in his eyes made me feel faint.

"You see, I always wear a bunch of white heliotrope; let me give this to you, that its smell may remind you of me tonight, and perhaps make you dream of me."

And taking the flowers from his

buttonhole, he put them into mine with one hand, whilst he slipped his left arm round my waist and clasped me tightly, pressing me against his whole body for a few seconds. That short space of time seemed to me an eternity.

I could feel his hot and panting breath against my lips. Below, our knees touched, and I felt something hard press and move against my thigh.

My emotion just then was such that I could hardly stand; for a moment I thought he would kiss me — nay, the crisp hair of his moustache was slightly tickling my lips, producing a most delightful sensation. However, he only looked deep into my eyes with a demoniac fascination.

I felt the fire of his glances sink deep into my breast, and far below. My blood began to boil and bubble like a burning fluid, so that I felt my — (what the Italians call a "birdie," and what they have portrayed as a winged cherub) — struggle within its prison, lift up its head, open its tiny lips, and again spout one or two drops of that creamy, life-giving fluid. But those few tears – far from being a soothing balm – seemed to be drops of caustic, burning me, and producing a strong, unbearable irritation. I was tortured. My mind was a hell. My body was on fire. Is he suffering as much as I am? said I to myself.

Just then he unclasped his arm from round my waist, and it fell lifeless of its own weight like that of a man asleep.

EROTICA OF THE
MIDDLE AGES

~•❧•~

Anticlericalism became a strong feature of erotica during the Middle Ages, as did voluptuous bawdiness. Compared to Europe and the rest of the world, English contribution to erotic literature during this time was fairly small but there was a growth in Welsh erotic poetry which was influenced by French verse (the pastourelle and the misogynistic fabliaux). The French cultural renaissance impacted strongly on Western erotic literature. One of the poems in this selection, "The Husband Who Saw his Wife with Another Man," was written by "Marie de France," the unidentified author of The Lais of Marie de France, *a collection of short poems that are supposed to be sung.*

from *The Penis (c. 1330–1350)*

≈

There is a pipe in your head,
a whistle for fucking every day.
There is an eye in your pate
which sees every woman as fair;
round pestle, expanding gun,
it is a searing fire to a small cunt;
roof-beam of girls' laps,
the swift growth is the clapper of a bell;
blunt pod, it dug a family,
snare of skin, nostril with a crop of two
    testicles.
You are a trouserful of wantonness,
your neck is leather, image of a goose's
    neckbone;
nature of complete falsity, pod of lewdness,
door-nail which causes a lawsuit and trouble.

Dafydd ap Gwilym (Mid 14th century)

The Husband Who Saw his
Wife with Another Man

~

A peasant lay in wait inside
His house to see what could be spied.
He saw another man instead
Of him, enjoying his wife in bed.
"Alas," he said, "what have I seen?"
His wife replied: "What do you mean?"
Fair lord, my love, what did you see?"
"Another man, I'm sure," said he,
"Was on the bed in your embrace."
His wife, with anger in her face,
Replied, "A man? Oh, very well,
You're sick again, that I can tell.
You cling to lies, as if they're true."
"I trust my eyes — that I must do."
"You're mad," she said "to think you can
Insist you saw me with a man.
Now tell the truth, at once, be good."
"I saw him leaving for the wood."
"Oh no!" she said, "that means that I

Today or next day'll surely die.
It happened to my Gran, you see,
My mother too, and now to me.
It happened just before they died –
A fact well-known both far and wide.
A young man led both off, you know –
They had no other cause to go.
My end is near, the die is cast –
Send for my cousins, I need them fast.
Let's split up all our property –
I mustn't waste my time, you see.
With all the stuff that is my share,
I'll to a nunnery repair."
The peasant heard, and cried in fear:
"Let be, let be, my sweetheart, dear,
Don't leave me now, like this, I pray –
I made up all I saw today."
"I dare not stay, it's far too late –
I'm thinking of my spiritual state,
Especially, after the shame
That you've attached to my good name.
I will be blamed, I know I will
For treating you so very ill,

Unless, perhaps, you'd rather swear,
With all my family standing there,
You never saw a man with me.
You must swear also, don't you see?
This subject will be dropped and you
Will never nag me for it, too."
He answered "Lady, I agree."
They both went off to church, and he
Soon swore to all she'd asked him for
All that, ah yes, and much much more.
Take warning from this tale, men, do,
That women know a thing or two –
For strange deceits and knavish tricks,
Their talent's greater than Old Nick's.

Marie de France (12th century)

THE DECAMERON

~

Written by Giovanni Boccaccio (1313–75), *The Decameron* is a collection of one hundred stories. Recounted by a group of rich, young patricians during ten days of the Black Death of 1348, it encompasses homosexuality, adultery and animal lust. Boccaccio wrote several other important works and inspired many writers and poets, including Shakespeare, Keats, Tennyson and George Eliot. This extract is taken from the Tenth Story of the Third Day and is translated by G. H. McWilliam.

from *The Decameron*

~

Alibech, the graceful young daughter of a rich man, leaves the comfort of her home in order to serve God. She meets Rustico, a monk, who assures her that the best way to serve the Almighty is to put the devil back in Hell. Rustico proceeds to divest himself of his clothes, whilst persuading Alibech to do the same.

In this posture the girl's beauty was displayed to Rustico in all its glory, and his longings blazed more fiercely than ever, bringing about the resurrection of the flesh. Alibech stared at this in amazement, and said:

"Rustico, what is that thing I see sticking out in front of you, which I do not possess?"

"Oh, my daughter," said Rustico, "this is the devil I was telling you about. Do you see what he's doing? He's hurting me so much that I can hardly endure it."

"Oh, praise be to God," said the girl, "I can see that I am better off than you are, for I have no such devil to contend with."

"You're right there," said Rustico. "But you have something else instead, that I haven't."

"Oh?" said Alibech. "And what's that?"

"You have Hell," said Rustico. "And I

honestly believe that God has sent you here for the salvation of my soul, because if this devil continues to plague the life out of me, and if you are prepared to take sufficient pity upon me to let me put him back into Hell, you will be giving me marvellous relief, as well as rendering incalculable service and pleasure to God, which is what you say you came here for to begin with."

"Oh, Father," replied the girl in all innocence, "if I really do have a Hell, let's do as you suggest just as soon as you are ready."

"God bless you, my daughter," said Rustico. "Let us go and put him back and then perhaps he'll leave me alone."

At which point he conveyed the girl to one of their beds, where he instructed her in the art of incarcerating that accursed fiend.

Never having put a single devil into Hell before, the girl found the first experience a little painful, and she said to Rustico:

"This devil must certainly be a bad lot, Father, and a true enemy of God, for as well as plaguing mankind, he even hurts Hell when he's driven back inside it."

"Daughter," said Rustico, "it will not always be like that." And in order to ensure that it wouldn't, before moving from the bed they put him back half a dozen times, curbing his arrogance to such good effect that he was positively glad to keep still for the rest of the day.

During the next few days, however, the devil's pride frequently reared its head again, and the girl, ever ready to obey the call to duty and bring him under control, happened to develop a taste for the sport, and began saying to Rustico:

"I can certainly see what those worthy men in Gafsa meant when they said that serving God was so agreeable. I don't honestly recall ever having done anything that gave me so much pleasure and satisfaction as I get from putting the devil back in Hell. To my way of thinking, anyone who devotes his energies to anything but the service of God is a complete blockhead."

She thus developed the habit of going to Rustico at frequent intervals, and saying to him:

"Father, I came here to serve God, not to idle away my time. Let's go and put the devil back in Hell."

And sometimes, in the middle of their labours, she would say:

"What puzzles me, Rustico, is that the devil should ever want to escape from Hell. Because if he liked being there as much as Hell enjoys receiving him and keeping him inside, he would never go away at all."

By inviting Rustico to play the game too often, continually urging him on in the service of God, the girl took so much stuffing out of him that he eventually began to turn cold where another man would have been bathed in sweat. So he told her that the devil should only be punished and put back in Hell when he reared his head with pride, adding that by the grace of Heaven, they had tamed him so effectively that he was pleading with God to be left in peace. In this way, he managed to keep the girl quiet for a while, but one day, having begun to notice that Rustico was no longer asking for the devil to be put back in Hell, she said:

"Look here, Rustico. Even though your devil has been punished and pesters you no longer, my Hell simply refuses to leave me alone. Now that I have helped you with my Hell to subdue the pride of your devil, the least you can do is to get your devil to help me tame the fury of my Hell."

Rustico, who was living on a diet of herb-roots and water, was quite incapable of supplying her requirements, and told her that the taming of her Hell would require an awful lot of devils, but promised to do what he could. Sometimes, therefore, he responded to the call, but this happened so infrequently that it was rather like chucking a bean into the mouth of a lion, with the result that the girl, who felt that she was not serving God as diligently as she would have liked, was found complaining more often than not.

THE CANTERBURY TALES

~

Geoffrey Chaucer (c. 1343–1400), arguably the most important medieval poet, began this great work in about 1386. The collection of tales told by pilgrims on their way to the shrine of Thomas à Becket ranges from the pious to the bawdy. It has been translated into modern English by Nevill Coghill.

from *The Wife of Bath's Prologue*

~

In marrying me suppose my husband dead;
There's nothing bigamous in such a bed.
Though it were good a man should never touch
    a woman (meaning here in bed and such)
And dangerous to assemble fire and tow
– What this allusion means you all must
    know –

He only says virginity is fresh,
More perfect than the frailty of the flesh
In married life – except when he and she
Prefer to live in married chastity.
I grant it you. I'll never say a word
Decrying maidenhood although preferred
To frequent marriage; there are those who
    mean
To live in their virginity, as clean
In body as in soul, and never mate.
I'll make no boast about my own estate.
As in a noble household, we are told,
Not every dish and vessel's made of gold,
Some are of wood, yet earn their master's
    praise,
God calls His folk to Him in many ways.
To each of them God gave His proper gift,
Some this, some that, and left them to make
    shift.
Virginity is indeed a great perfection,
And married continence, for God's
    dilection,
But Christ, who of perfection is the well,

Bade not that everyone should go and sell
All that he had and give it to the poor
To follow in His footsteps, that is sure.
He spoke to those that would live perfectly,
And by your leave, my lords, that's not for
    me.
I will bestow the flower of life, the honey,
Upon the acts and fruit of matrimony.
Tell me to what conclusion or in aid
Of what were generative organs made?
And for what profit were those creatures
    wrought?
Trust me, they cannot have been made for
    naught.
Gloze as you will and plead the explanation
That they were only made for the purgation
Of urine, little things of no avail
Except to know a female from a male,
And nothing else. Did somebody say no?
Experience knows well it isn't so.
The learned may rebuke me, or be loath
To think it so, but they were made for both,
That is to say both use and pleasure in

Engendering, except in case of sin.
Why else the proverb written down and set
In books: "A man must yield his wife her
    debt?"
What means of paying her can he invent
Unless he use his silly instrument?
It follows they were fashioned at creation
Both to purge urine and for propagation.

from *Grand Testament*

〜

I love and serve my lady with a will,
but that's no reason you should call me mad.
For her, I'd hitch on sword and shield to kill.
She is the goods to please my every fad.
When customers arrive, I lightly pad
to bring in pots and wine. I serve them
    cheese
and fruit, and bread and water as they please
and say (depending on the tip I'm paid)
"Do call again and come here at your ease

in this whorehouse where we do a roaring
    trade."

But then fine feelings end and turn to ill.
When she comes home without the cash, I'm
    had.
I cannot stand her, she has blood to spill.
I hate her, grab her belt, gown, shift and
    plaid
and swear I'll flog the lot and her to add
up for the loss of all the nightly fees.
But hands on hips she hollers if you please
how I am anti-Christ and won't get paid.
I grab a club and sign her, nose to knees,
in this whorehouse where we do a roaring
    trade.

We make peace then in bed. She takes my
    fill,
gorged like a dung-beetle, blows me a bad
and mighty poisonous fart. I fit her bill
she says, and laughing bangs my nob quite
    glad.

She thwacks my thigh and, after what we've
    had,
dead drunk we sleep like logs – and let the
    fleas.
Though when we stir her quim begins to
    tease.
She mounts: I groan beneath the weight –
    I'm splayed!
Her screwing soon will bring me to my knees
in this whorehouse where we do a roaring
    trade.

Vary the wind, come frost, I live in ease.
I am a fucker; she fucks as I please.
Layman or laity – no matter of degrees!
Layer on layer of onion overlaid,
Our filth we love and filths upon us seize;
Now we flee honour, honour from us flees
in this whorehouse where we do a roaring
    trade.

              François Villon (1431–85)

A SHORT STORY

This extract from *The Perfumed Garden* is a perfect example of the delightful erotic poetry in this 16th-century book on the art of love.

The History of Djoâidi and Fadehat el Djemal

I was in love with a woman who was all grace and perfection, beautiful of shape, and gifted with all imaginable charms. Her cheeks were like roses, her forehead lily white, her lips like coral; she had teeth like pearls, and breasts like pomegranates. Her mouth opened round like a ring; her tongue seemed to be incrusted with precious gems; her eyes, black and finely slit, had the languor of slumber, and her voice the sweetness of sugar. With her form pleasantly filled out, her flesh was mellow like fresh butter, and pure as the diamond.

As to her vulva, it was white, prominent, round as an arch, the centre of it was red, and breathed fire, without a trace of humidity; for, sweet to the touch, it was quite dry. When she walked it showed in relief like a dome or an inverted cup. In reclining it was visible between her thighs, looking like a kid couched on a hillock.

This woman was my neighbour. All the others played and laughed with me, jested with me, and met my suggestions with great pleasure. I revelled in their kisses, their close embraces and nibbling, and in sucking their lips, breasts, and necks. I had coition with all of them, except my neighbour, and it was exactly her I wanted to possess in preference to all the rest; but instead of being kind to me, she avoided me rather. When I contrived to take her aside to trifle with her and try to rouse her gaiety, and spoke to her of my desires, she recited to me the following verses, the sense of which was a mystery to me:

Among the mountain tops I saw a tent
    placed firmly,
Apparent to all eyes high up in mid-air.
But, oh! The pole that held it up was gone.
And like a vase without a handle it
    remained,
With all its cords undone, its centre
    sinking in,
Forming a hollow like that of a kettle.

Every time I told her of my passion she answered me with these verses, which to me were void of meaning, and to which I could make no reply, which, however, only excited my love all the more. I therefore inquired of all those I knew – amongst wise men, philosophers, and savants – the meaning, but not one of them could solve the riddle for me, so as to satisfy my heat and appease my passion.

Nevertheless I continued my investigations, until at last I heard of a savant named Abou Nouass, who lived in a far-off country, and who, I was told, was the only man capable of solving the enigma. I betook to him, apprised him of the distress I had with the woman, and recited to him the abovementioned verses.

Abou Nouass said to me, "This woman loves you to the exclusion of every other man. She is very corpulent and plump." I answered, "It is exactly as you say. You have given her likeness as if she were before you, excepting what you say in respect of her love for me, for, until now, she has never given me any proof of it."

"She has no husband."

"This is so," I said.

Then he added, "I have reason to believe that your member is of small dimensions,

and such a member cannot give her pleasure
nor quench her fire; for what she wants is a
lover with a member like that of an ass.
Perhaps It may not be so. Tell me the truth
about this!" When I had reassured him on
that point, affirming that my member, which
began to rise at the expression of his
doubtings, was full-sized, he told me that in
that case all difficulties would disappear, and
explained to me the sense of the verses as
follows:

"The *tent*, firmly planted, represents the
vulva of grand dimension and placed well
forward, the *mountains*, between which it
rises, are the thighs. The *stake* which
supported its centre and has been torn up
means that she has no husband, comparing
the stake or pole that supports the tent to the
virile member holding up the lips of the vulva.
She is like a vase without a handle; this means if
the pail is without a handle to hang it up by it
is good for nothing, the pail representing the
vulva, and the handle the verge. *The cords are*

undone and its centre is sinking in; that is to say, as the tent without a supporting pole caves in at the centre, inferior in this respect to the vault which remains upright without support, so can the woman who has no husband not enjoy complete happiness. From the words, *It forms a hollow like that of a kettle*, you may judge how lascivious God has made that woman in her comparisons; she likens her vulva to a kettle, which serves to prepare the *tserid*. Listen; if the *tserid* is placed in the kettle, to turn out well it must be stirred by means of a *medeleuk*, long and solid, whilst the kettle is steadied by the feet and hands. Only in that way can it be properly prepared. It cannot be done with a small spoon; the cook would burn her hands, owing to the shortness of the handle, and the dish would not be well prepared. This is the symbol of this woman's nature, O Djoaidi. If your member has not the dimensions of a respectable *medeleuk*, serviceable for the good preparation of the *tserid*, it will not give her satisfaction, and, moreover, if you do not hold her close to your chest, enlacing her with your hands and feet, it is useless to solicit her favours; finally if you let her consume herself by her own fire, like the bottom of the kettle which gets burnt if the *medeleuk* is not stirred upon it, you will not gratify her desire by the result.

"You see now what prevented her from acceding to your wishes; she was afraid that you would not be able to quench her flame after having fanned it.

"But what is the name of this woman, O Djoâidi?"

"Fadehat el Djemal," (the sunrise of beauty), I replied.

"Return to her," said the sage, "and take her these verses, and your affair will come to a happy issue, please God! You will then come back to me, and inform me of what will have come to pass between you two."

I gave my promise, and Abou Nouass recited to me the following lines:

Have patience now, O Fadehat el Djemal,
I understand your words, and all shall see
   how I obey them.
O you! Beloved and cherished by whoever
Can revel in your charms and glory in
   them!
O apple of my eye! You thought I was
   embarrassed
About the answer which I had to give you.
Yes, certainly! It was the love I bore you
Made me look foolish in the eyes of all
   you know.
They thought I was possessed of a demon;
Called me a Merry Andrew and buffoon.
For God! What of buffoonery I've got,
Should it be that
No other member is like mine? Here! See
   it, measure it!
What woman tastes it falls in love with
   me,
In violent love. It is a well-known fact
That you from far may see it like a
   column.

If it erects itself it lifts my robe and
    shames me.
Now take it kindly, put it in your tent,
Which is between the well-known
    mountains placed.
It will be quite at home there, you will find
    it
Not softening while inside, but sticking
    like a nail;
Take it to form a handle to your vase.
Come and examine it, and notice well
How vigorous it is and long in its
    erection!
If you but want a proper *medeleuk*,
A *medeleuk* to use between your thighs,
Take this to stir the centre of your kettle.
It will do good to you, O mistress mine!
Your kettle be it plated will be satisfied!

Having learnt these verses by heart, I took
my leave of Abou Nouass and returned to
Fadehat el Djemal. She was, as usual, alone.
I gave a slight knock at her door; she came
out at once, beautiful as the rising sun, and

coming up to me, she said, "Oh! Enemy of God, what business has brought you here to me at this time?"

I answered her, "O my mistress! a business of great importance."

"Explain yourself, and I will see whether I can help you," she said.

"I shall not speak to you about it until the door is locked," I answered.

"Your boldness today is very great," she said.

And I, "True, O my mistress! boldness is one of my qualities."

She then addressed me thus, "O enemy of yourself! O you most miserable of your race! If I were to lock the door, and you have nothing wherewith to satisfy my desires, what should I do with you? face of a Jew!"

"You will let me share your couch, and grant me your favours."

She began to laugh; and after we had entered the house, she told a slave to lock the house door. As usual, I asked her to respond to my proposals; she then recited to me again the above-mentioned verses;. When she had finished I began to recite to her those which Abou Nouass had taught me.

As I proceeded I saw her more and more moved, I observed her giving way to yawns, to stretch herself, to sigh. I knew now I should arrive at the desired result. When I had finished, my member was in such a state of erection that it became like a pillar, still lengthening. When Fadehat el Djemal saw it in that condition she precipitated herself upon it, took it into her hands, and drew it towards her thighs. I then said, "O apple of my eyes! this may not be done here, let us go into your chamber."

She replied, "Leave me alone, O son of a debauched woman! Before God! I am losing my senses in seeing your member getting longer and longer, and lifting your robe. Oh, what a member! I never saw a finer one! Let it penetrate into this delicious, plump vulva, which maddens all who hear it described; for the sake of which so many have died of love; and of which your superiors and masters themselves have not been able to get possession."

I repeated, "I shall not do it anywhere else than in your chamber."

She answered, "If you do not enter this minute this tender vulva, I shall die."

As I still insisted upon repairing to her room, she cried, "No, it is quite impossible, I cannot wait so long!"

I saw in fact her lips tremble, her eyes filling with tears. A general tremor ran over her, she changed colour, and laid herself down upon her back, baring her thighs, the whiteness of which made her flesh appear like crystal tinged with carmine.

Then I examined her vulva – a white cupola with a purple centre, soft and charming. It opened like that of a mare on the approach of a stallion.

At the moment she seized my member and kissed it, saying, "By the religion of my father! it must penetrate into my vulva!" and drawing nearer to me she pulled it towards her vagina.

I now hesitated no longer to assist her with my member, and placed it against the entrance to her vulva. As soon as the head of my member touched the lips, the whole body of Fadehat el Djemal trembled with excitement. Sighing and sobbing, she held me pressed to her bosom.

Again I profited by this moment to admire the beauties of her vulva. It was magnificent, its purple centre setting off its whiteness all the more. It was round, and without any imperfection; projecting like a splendidly curved dome over her belly. In one word, it was a masterpiece of creation as fine as could be seen. The blessing of God, the best creator, upon it.

And the woman who possessed this wonder had in her time no superior.

Seeing her then in such transports, trembling like a bird, the throat of which is being cut, I pushed my dart into her. Thinking she might not be able to take in the whole of my member, I had entered cautiously, but she moved her buttocks furiously, saying to me, "This is not enough for my contentment." Making a strong push, I lodged my member completely in her, which made her utter a painful cry, but the moment after she moved with greater fury than before. She cried, "Do not miss the corners, neither high nor low, but above all things do not neglect the centre! The centre!" she repeated. "If you feel it coming, let it go into my matrix so as to extinguish my fire." Then we moved alternately in and out, which was delicious. Our legs were interlaced, our muscles unbent, and so we went on with kisses and claspings until the crisis came upon us simultaneously. We then rested and took breath after this mutual conflict.

I wanted to withdraw my member, but she would not consent to this and begged of me not to take it out. I acceded to her wish, but a moment later she took it out herself, dried it, and replaced it in her vulva. We renewed our game, kissing, pressing, and moving in rhythm. After a short time, we rose and entered her chamber, without having this time accomplished the enjoyment. She gave me now a piece of an aromatic root, which she recommended me to keep in my mouth, assuring me that as long as I had it there my member would remain on the alert. Then she asked me to lie down, which I did. She mounted upon me, and taking my member into her hands, she made it enter entirely into her vagina. I was astonished at the vigour of her vulva and at the heat emitted from it. The opening of her matrix in particular excited my admiration. I never had any experience like it; it closely clasped my member and pinched the gland.

With the exception of Fadehat el Djemal no woman had until then taken in my member to its full length. She was able to do so, I believe, owing to her being very plump and corpulent, and her vulva being large and deep.

Fadehat el Djemal, astride upon me, began to rise and descend; she kept crying out, wept, went slower, then accelerated her movements again, ceased to move altogether; when part of my member became visible she looked at it, then took it out altogether to examine it closely, then plunged it in again until it had disappeared completely. So she continued until the enjoyment overcame her again. At last, having dismounted from me, she now laid herself down, and asked me to get on to her. I did so, and she introduced my member entirely into her vulva.

We thus continued our caresses, changing our positions in turns, until night came on. I thought it proper to show a wish to go now, but she would not agree to this, and I had to give her my word that I would remain. I said to myself, "This woman will not let me go at any price, but when daylight comes God will advise me." I remained with her, and all night long we kept caressing each other, and took but scant rest.

I counted that during that day and night, I accomplished twenty-seven times the act of coitus, and I became afraid that I should nevermore be able to leave the house of that woman.

Having at last made good my escape, I went to visit Abou Nouass again, and informed him of all that had happened. He was surprised and stupefied, and his first words were, "O Djoâidi, you can have neither authority nor power over such a woman, and she would make you do penance for all the pleasure you have had with other women!"

However, Fadehat el Djemal proposed to me to become her legitimate husband, in order to put a stop to the vexatious rumours that were circulating about her conduct. I, on the other hand, was only on the look out for adultery. Asking the advice of Abou Nouass about it, he told me, "If you marry

Fadehat el Djemal you will ruin your health, and God will withdraw his protection from you, and the worst of all will be that she will cuckold you, for she is insatiable with respect to the coitus, and would cover you with shame." And I answered him, "Such is the nature of women; they are insatiable as far as their vulvas are concerned, and so long as their lust is satisfied they do not care whether it be with a buffoon, a negro, a valet, or even with a man that is despised and reprobated by society."

On this occasion Abou Nouass depicted the character of women in the following verses:

Women are demons, and were born as
    such;
No one can trust them, as is known to all;
If they love a man, it is only out of
    caprice;
And he to whom they are most cruel loves
    them most;

Beings full of treachery and trickery, I
aver
The man that loves you truly is a lost
man;
He who believes me not can prove my
word
By letting woman's love get hold of him
for years!
If in your own generous mood you have
given them
Your all and everything for years and
years,
They will say afterwards, "I swear by God!
My eyes
have never seen a thing he gave me!"
After you have impoverished yourself for
their sake,
Their cry from day to day will be for ever,
"Give!
Give, man. Get up and buy and borrow."
If they cannot profit by you they'll turn
against you;
They will tell lies about you and

calumniate you.

They do not recoil to use a slave in the
master's absence,

If once their passions are aroused, and
they play tricks;

Assuredly, if once their vulva is in rut,

They only think of getting in some
member in erection.

Preserve us, God! from woman's trickery;

And of old women in particular. So be it.